STUDENT'S
SOLUTIONS MANUAL
SHARON MYERS

PROBABILITY & STATISTICS
FOR ENGINEERS & SCIENTISTS

SEVENTH
EDITION

WALPOLE · MYERS · MYERS · YE

UPPER SADDLE RIVER, NJ 07458

Editor in Chief: Sally Yagan
Acquisitions Editor: Quincy McDonald
Supplement Editor: Joanne Wendelken
Assistant Managing Editor, Math Media Production: John Matthews
Production Editor: Donna Crilly
Supplement Cover Manager: Paul Gourhan
Supplement Cover Designer: PM Workshop Inc.
Manufacturing Buyer: Ilene Kahn

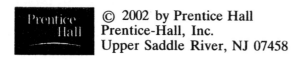

Printed in the United States of America

10 9 8 7 6 5

ISBN 0-13-041537-5

Pearson Education Ltd., *London*
Pearson Education Australia Pty. Ltd., *Sydney*
Pearson Education Singapore, Pte. Ltd.
Pearson Education North Asia Ltd., *Hong Kong*
Pearson Education Canada, Inc., *Toronto*
Pearson Educacíon de Mexico, S.A. de C.V.
Pearson Education—Japan, *Tokyo*
Pearson Education Malaysia, Pte. Ltd.

Contents

Chapter 1
Introduction to Statistics and Data Analysis

Section 1.8 Graphical Methods and Data Description

1.   (a)   Mean = 124.3, median = 120;
       (b)   175 is an extreme observation.

3.   (a)   Smokers mean = 43.70; nonsmokers mean = 30.32.
       (b)   Smokers standard deviation = 16.93;
             nonsmokers standard deviation = 7.13.
       (d)   SNNSSNNNNNNNNSNNNNNSSSSSSSS

   $$\uparrow \qquad\qquad \uparrow$$
   $$\bar{x}_N \qquad\qquad \bar{x}_S$$

       (d)   Smokers appear to take longer to fall asleep.
             For smokers the time to fall asleep is more variable.

5.   Yes. P-value = 0.03125.
       The outcome HHHHH would be very unlikely with a fair coin.

7.   (a)

Stem	Leaf	Frequency
0	22233457	8
1	023558	6
2	035	3
3	03	2
4	057	3
5	0569	4
6	0005	4

       (b)   Relative Frequency Distribution of Years

Class Interval	Class Midpoint	Frequency f	Relative Frequency
0.0 - 0.9	0.45	8	0.267
1.0 - 1.9	1.45	6	0.200
2.0 - 2.9	2.45	3	0.100
3.0 - 3.9	3.45	2	0.067
4.0 - 4.9	4.45	3	0.100
5.0 - 5.9	5.45	4	0.133
6.0 - 6.9	6.45	4	0.133

       (c)   Sample mean = 2.80; sample range = 6.3;
             sample standard deviation = 2.2273

9.   (a)   Sample mean = 1.77; sample median = 1.77.
       (b)   Sample standard deviation = 0.3904.

11. (a) 999999999989899888989989988888889899988···8888

(b) $\bar{x}_9 = 160.15$ $\bar{x}_8 = 395.10$

(c) The sample mean for 1980 is over twice as large as that of 1990. The variability for 1990 decreased also as seen by looking at the picture in (a). The gap represents an increase of over 400 ppm. It appears from the data that hydrocarbon emissions decreased considerably between 1980 and 1990 and that the extremely large emissions (over 500 ppm) were no longer in evidence.

Chapter 2
Probability

Section 2.2 Events

1. (a) S = {8, 16, 24, 32, 40, 48}.
   (b) $x^2 + 4x - 5 = (x + 5)(x - 1) = 0$. Hence x = –5 and x = 1 are the only solutions.
      S = {–5, 1}.
   (c) S = (T, HT, HHT, HHH}.
   (d) S = {N. America, S. America, Europe, Asia, Africa, Australia, Antartica}.
   (e) Solving $2x - 4 \geq 0$ gives $x \geq 2$. Since we must also have x < 1.

3. (a) A = {1, 3}.
   (b) B = {1, 2, 3, 4, 5, 6}.
   (c) $C = \{x \mid x^2 - 4x + 3 = 0\} = \{x \mid (x - 1)(x - 3) = 0\} = \{1, 3\}$.
      Clearly A = C.
   (d) D = {0, 1, 2, 3, 4, 5, 6}

5. S = {1HH, 1HT, 1TH, 1TT, 2H, 2T, 3HH, 3HT, 3TH, 3TT, 4H, 4T, 5HH, 5HT, 5TH, 5TT, 6H, 6T}.

7. S_1 = {MMMM, MMMF, MMFM, MFMM, FMMM, MMFF, MFMF, MFFM, FMFM, FFMM, FMMF, MFFF, FMFF, FFMF, FFFM, FFFF}.
   S_2 = {0, 1, 2, 3, 4}.

9. (a) A = {1HH, 1HT, 1TH, 1TT, 2H, 2T}.
   (b) B = {1TT, 3TT, 5TT}.
   (c) A' = {3HH, 3HT, 3TH, 3TT, 4H, 4T, 5HH, 5HT, 5TH, 5TT, 6H, 6T}.
   (d) (A' ∩ B) = {3TT, 5TT}.
   (e) (A ∪ B) = {1HH, 1HT, 1TH, 1TT, 2H, 2T, 3TT, 5TT}.

11. (a) S = {M_1M_2, M_1F_1, M_1F_2, M_2M_1, M_2F_1, M_2F_2, F_1M_1, F_1M_2, F_1F_2, F_2M_1, F_2M_2, F_2F_1}.
    (b) A = {M_1M_2, M_1F_1, M_1F_2, M_2M_1, M_2F_1, M_2F_2}.
    (c) B = {M_1F_1, M_1F_2, M_2F_1, M_2F_2, F_1M_1, F_1M_2, F_2M_1, F_2M_2}.
    (d) C = {F_1F_2, F_2F_1}.
    (e) (A ∩ B) = {M_1F_1, M_1F_2, M_2F_1, M_2F_2}.
    (f) (A ∪ C) = {M_1M_2, M_1F_1, M_1F_2, M_2M_1, M_2F_1, M_2F_2, F_1F_2, F_2F_1}.

    (g)

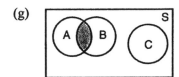

13.

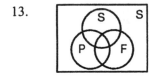

3

15. (a) $A' = $ {nitrogen, potassium, uranium, oxygen}.

    (b) $A \cup C = $ {copper, sodium, zinc, oxygen}.

    (c) $B' = $ {copper, uranium, oxygen, zinc.}, $A \cap B' = $ {copper, zinc}, $C' = $ {copper, sodium, nitrogen, potassium, uranium, zinc}, $(A \cap B') \cup C' = $ {copper, sodium, nitrogen, potassium, uranium, zinc}.

    (d) $B' \cap C' = $ {copper, uranium, zinc}.

    (e) $A \cap B \cap C = \varnothing$.

    (f) $A' \cup B' = $ {nitrogen, potassium, uranium, oxygen, copper, zinc}.
       $A' \cap C = $ {oxygen}.
       $(A' \cup B') \cap (A' \cap C) = $ {oxygen}.

17. (a) $(A \cap B)' = $

    (b) $(A \cup B)' = $

    (c) $(A \cap C) \cup B = $

19. (a) The family will experience mechanical problems, but will receive no ticket for a traffic violation and will not arrive at a campsite having no vacancies.

    (b) The family will receive a traffic ticket and arrive at a campsite having no vacancies, but will not experience mechanical problems.

    (c) The family will experience mechanical problems and will arrive at a campsite having no vacancies.

    (d) The family will receive a traffic ticket, but will not arrive at a campsite having no vacancies.

    (e) The family will not experience mechanical problems.

Section 2.3 Counting Sample Points

1. With $n_1 = 6$ sightseeing tours each available on $n_2 = 3$ different days, the multiplication rule give $n_1 n_2 = (6)(3) = 18$ ways for a person to arrange a tour.

3. Since the die can land in $n_1 = 6$ ways and a letter can be selected in $n_2 = 26$ ways, the multiplication rule gives $n_1 n_2 = (6)(26) = 156$ points in S.

4

5. With $n_1 = 5$ different show styles in $n_2 = 4$ different colors, the multiplication rule gives $n_1 n_2 = (5)(4) = 20$ different pairs of shoes.

7. Using the generalized multiplication rule, there are $n_1 \times n_2 \times n_3 \times n_4 = 4 \times 3 \times 2 \times 2 = 48$ different house plans available.

9. With $n_1 = 3$ race cars, $n_2 = 5$ brands of gasoline, $n_3 = 7$ test sites, and $n_4 = 2$ drivers, the generalized multiplication rule yields $n_1 \times n_2 \times n_3 \times n_4 = 3 \times 5 \times 7 \times 2 = 210$ test runs.

11. (a) With $n_4 = 4$ possible answers for the first question, $n_2 = 4$ possible answers for the second question, and so forth, the generalized multiplication rule yields $n_1 \times n_2 \times n_3 \times n_4 \times n_5 = 4 \times 4 \times 4 \times 4 \times 4 = 1024$ ways to answer the test.

    (b) With $n_1 = 3$ wrong answers for the first question, $n_2 = 3$ wrong answers to the second question, and so forth, the generalized multiplication rule yields $n_1 \times n_2 \times n_3 \times n_4 \times n_5 = 3 \times 3 \times 3 \times 3 \times 3 = 243$ ways to answer the test and get all questions wrong.

13. Since the first digit is a 5, there are $n_1 = 9$ possibilities for the second digit and then $n_2 = 8$ possibilities for the third digit. Therefore, by the multiplication rule there are $(n_1)(n_2) = (9)(8) = 72$ registrations to be checked.

15. The first house can be placed on any of the $n_1 = 9$ lots, the second house on any of the remaining $n_2 = 8$ lots, and so forth. By Theorem 2.3 there are $9! = 362,880$ ways to place the 9 homes on the 9 lots.

17. The first seat must be filled with any of 5 girls and the second seat by any of 4 boys. Continuing in this manner, the total number of ways to seat the 5 girls and 4 boys is $(5)(4)(4)(3)(3)(2)(2)(1)(1) = 2880$.

19. (a) Any of the $n_1 = 8$ finalists may come in first, any of the $n_2 = 7$ remaining finalists can then come in second, and so forth. By Theorem 2.3, there are $8! = 40,320$ possible orders in which the 8 finalists may finish the spelling bee.

    (b) The possible orders for the first 3 positiions are $_8P_3 = 8!/5! = 336$.

21. By Theorem 2.7,
$$_6P_4 = \frac{6!}{2!} = 360.$$

23. By Theorem 2.5, $4! = 24$.

25. By Theorem 2.6,
$$\frac{8!}{3!2!} = 3360.$$

27. By Theorem 2.7,
$$\binom{12}{7,3,2} = 7920.$$

5

29.   By Theorem 2.8

$$\binom{8}{3} = 56.$$

Section 2.5 Additive Rule

1.   (a)   Sum of the probabilities exceeds 1.
      (b)   Sum of the probabilities is less than 1.
      (c)   A negative probability.
      (d)   Probability of both a heart and a black card is zero.

3.   S = {$10.00, $25.00, $100.00}, with weights 275/500 = 11/20, 150/500 = 3/10, and 75/500 = 3/20, respectively. The probability that the first envelope purchased contains less than $100.00 is equal to 11/20 + 3/10 = 17/20.

5.   Consider the events

      M: Industry will locate in Munich
      B: Industry will locate in Brussels
      (a) $P(M \cap B) = P(M) + P(B) - P(M \cup B) = 0.7 + 0.4 - 0.8 = 0.3.$
      (b) $P(M' \cap B') = P(M') + P(B') - P(M' \cup B') = 1.0 - P(M \cup B) = 1.0 - 0.8 = 0.2.$

7.   (a)   Since 5 of the 26 letters are vowels, we get a probability of 5/26.
      (b)   Since 9 of the 26 letters precede j, we get a probability of 9/26.
      (c)   Since 19 of the 26 letters follow g, we get a probability of 19/16.

9.   By Theorem 2.2 there are N = (26)(25)(24)(9)(8)(7)(6) = 47,174,400 possible ways to code the items of which n = (5)(25)(24)(8)(7)(6)(4) = 4,032,000 begin with a vowel and end with an even digit. Therefore, n/N = 10/117.

11.   Since there are 20 cards greater than 2 and less than 8, the probability of selecting two of these in succession is

$$\left(\frac{20}{32}\right)\left(\frac{19}{51}\right) = \left(\frac{95}{663}\right).$$

13.   (a) $\dfrac{\binom{4}{3}\binom{48}{2}}{\binom{52}{5}} = \dfrac{94}{54{,}145}.$ $\dfrac{\binom{13}{4}\binom{13}{1}}{\binom{52}{5}} = \dfrac{143}{39{,}984}.$

15.

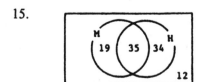

(a) $P(M \cup H) = 88/100 = 22/25$.
(b) $P(M' \cap H') = 12/100 = 3/25$.
(c) $P(H \cap M') = 34/100 = 17/50$.

17. (a) 0.32;   (b) 0.68;   (c) office or den

Section 2.7 Multiplicative Rule

1.   (a) The probability that a convict who pushed dope, also committed armed robbery.
     (b) The probability that a convict who committed armed robbery, did not push dope.
     (c) The probability that a convict who did not push dope also did not commit armed robbery.

3.   Consider the events
        M: a person is a male,
        S: a person has a secondary education,
        C: a person has a college degree.

     (a) $P(M \mid S) = 28/78 = 14/39$.
     (b) $P(C' \mid M') = 95/112$.

5.

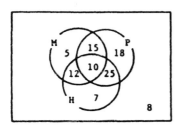

     (a) $P(M \cap P \cap H \mid P) = 10/68 = 5/34$.
     (b) $P(II \cap M \mid P') = 12/32 = 3/8$.

7.   (a) 0.018
     (b) $0.022 + 0.002 + 0.160 + 0.102 + 0.046 + 0.084 = 0.614$
     (c) $0.102/0.614 = 0.166$
     (d) $(0.102 + 0.046)/(0.175 + 0.134) = 0.479$

9.   Consider the events
        H: Husband watches a certain show.
        W: Wife watches the same show.

     (a) $P(W \cap H) = P(W)P(H \mid W) = (0.5)(0.7) = 0.35$.
     (b) $P(W \mid H) = P(W \cap H)/P(H) = 0.35/0.4 = 0.875$.
     (c) $P(W \cup H) = P(W) + P(H) - P(W \cap H)$
                     $= 0.5 + 0.4 - 0.35 = 0.55$.

7

11. Consider the events

A: the vehicle is a camper.

B: the vehicle has Canadian license plates.

(a) $P(B \mid A) = P(A \cap B)/P(A) = 0.09/0.28 = 9/28$.

(b) $P(A \mid B) = P(A \cap B)/P(B) = 0.09/0.12 = 3/4$.

(c) $P(B' \cup A') = 1 - P(A \cap B) = 1 - 0.09 = 0.91$.

13. Consider the events

A: the doctor makes a correct diagnosis,

B: the patient sues.

$P(A' \cap B) = P(A')P(B \mid A') = (0.3)(0.9) = 0.27$.

15. Consider the events:

A: the house is open

B: the correct key is selected

$$P(B) = \frac{\binom{1}{1}\binom{7}{2}}{\binom{8}{3}} = \frac{3}{8} = 0.375$$

$P(A) = 0.4$, $P(A') = 0.6$,

$P[A \cup (A' \cap B)] = P(A) + P(A')P(B) = 0.4 + (0.6)(0.375) = 0.625$.

17. Let A and B represent the availability of each fire engine.

(a) $P[A' \cap B'] = P(A')P(B') = (0.04)(0.04) = 0.0016$.

$P(A \cup B) = 1. - P(A' \cap B') = 1. - 0.0016 = 0.9984$.

19. Consider the events

A_1: aspirin tablets are selected from the overnight case,

A_2: aspirin tablets are selected from the tote bag.

L_2: laxative tablets are selected from the tote bag,

T_1: thyroid tablets are selected from the overnight case,

T_2: thyroid tablets are selected from the tote bag.

(a) $P(T_1 \cap T_2) = P(T_1)P(T_2) = (3/5)(2/6) = 1/5$.

(b) $P(T_1' \cap T_2') = P(T_1')P(T_2') = (2/5)(4/6) = 4/15$.

(c) $1 - P(A_1 \cap A_2) - P(T_1 \cap T_2) = 1 - P(A_1)P(A_2) - P(T_1)P(T_2)$
$= 1 - (2/5)(3/6) - (3/5)(2/6) = 3/5$.

21. (a) $P(Q_1 \cap Q_2 \cap Q_3 \cap Q_4) = P(Q_1)P(Q_2 \mid Q_1)P(Q_3 \mid Q_1 \cap Q_2)P(Q_4 \mid Q_1 \cap Q_2 Q_3) =$
$(15/20)(14/19)(13/18)(12/17) = 91/323$.

(b) Let A be the event that 4 good quarts of milk are selected.
Then

$$P(A) = \frac{\binom{15}{4}}{\binom{20}{4}} = 91/323.$$

8

23. This is a parallel system of two series subsystems.

(a) $P = 1 - (1 - (0.7)(0.7))(1 - (0.8)(0.8)(0.8)) = 0.7511$.

(b) $P = \dfrac{P(A' \cap C \cap D \cap E)}{P(\text{Systems works})} = \dfrac{(0.7)(0.8)(0.8)(0.8)}{0.75112} = 0.4772$.

Section 2.8 Bayes' Rule

1. Consider the events
   C: an adult selected has cancer
   D: the adult is diagnosed as having cancer
   $P(C) = 0.05$. $P(D \mid C) = 0.78$ $P(C') = 0.95$ $P(D \mid C') = 0.06$
   $P(C \cap D) = (0.05)(0.78) = 0.039$ $P(C' \cap D) = (0.95)(0.06) = 0.057$
   $P(D) = P(C \cap D) = P(C' \cap D) = 0.096$.

3. $P(C \mid D) = P(C \cap D)/P(D) = 0.039/0.096$.

5. Consider the events
   A: no expiration date
   B_1: John is the inspector $P(B_1) = 0.20$ $P(A \mid B_1) = 0.005$ $P(B_1)P(A \mid B_1) = 0.0010$
   B_2: Tom is the inspector $P(B_2) = 0.60$ $P(A \mid B_2) = 0.010$ $P(B_2)P(A \mid B_2) = 0.0060$
   B_3: Jeff is the inspector $P(B_3) = 0.15$ $P(A \mid B_3) = 0.011$ $P(B_3)P(A \mid B_3) = 0.0017$
   B_4: Pat is the inspector $P(B_4) = 0.05$ $P(A \mid B_4) = 0.005$ $P(B_4)P(A \mid B_4) = \underline{0.0002}$

   $\hfill 0.0089$

   $$P(B_1 \mid A) = \frac{P(B_1)P(A \mid B_1)}{P(B_1)P(A \mid B_1) + P(B_2)P(A \mid B_{21}) + P(B_3)P(A \mid B_3) + P(B_4)P(A \mid B_4)} = \frac{0.0010}{0.0089}$$
   $$= 0.1124$$

7. (a) $P(A \cap B \cap C) = P(C \mid A \cap B) = (0.20)(0.225) = 0.045$

   (b) $P(A \cap B') = P(B' \mid A)P(A) = (0.25)(0.3) = 0.075$;
   $P(A' \cap B') = P(B' \mid A')P(A') = (0.80)(0.70) = 0.56$.
   $P(B' \cap C) = P(A \cap B' \cap C) + P(A' \cap B' \cap C)$
   $\qquad = P(C \mid A \cap B')P(A \cap B') + P(C \mid A' \cap B')P(A' \cap B')$
   $\qquad = (0.80)(0.075) + (0.90)(0.56)$
   $\qquad = 0.564$.

   (c) $P(A' \cap B) = P(B \mid A')P(A') = (0.20)(0.7) = 0.14$
   From (a) $P(A \cap B \cap C) = 0.045$
   $P(A' \cap B \cap C) = P(C \mid A' \cap B)P(A' \cap B) = (0.15)(0.14) = 0.021$
   $P(A \cap B' \cap C) = P(C \mid A \cap B')P(A \cap B') = (0.80)(0.075) = 0.060$.
   $P(A' \cap B' \cap C) = P(C \mid A' \cap B')P(A' \cap B') = (0.90)(0.56) = 0.504$
   $P(C) = 0.045 + 0.021 + 0.060 + 0.504 = 0.630$.

   (d) $P(A \mid B' \cap C) = P(A \cap B' \cap C)/P(B' \cap C) = 0.06/(0.564) = 0.1064$.

Chapter 3
Random Variables and Probability Distributions

Section 3.3 Continuous Probability Distributions

1.   Discrete: continuous; continuous; discrete; discrete; continuous.

3.

Sample Space	w
HHH	3
HHT	1
HTH	1
THH	1
HTT	−1
THT	−1
TTH	−1
TTT	−3

5.   (a) $1 = \sum\limits_{x=0}^{3} c(x^2 + 4) = 30c$. Therefore $c = 1/30$.

       (b) $1 = \sum\limits_{x=0}^{2} c\binom{2}{x}\binom{3}{3-x} = c\left[\binom{2}{0}\binom{3}{3} + \binom{2}{1}\binom{3}{2} + \binom{2}{2}\binom{3}{1}\right]$
           $= 10c$. Therefore $c = 1/10$.

7.   (a) $P(X < 1.2) = \int_{0}^{1} x\, dx + \int_{1}^{1.2} (2-x)dx$

           $= \left.\dfrac{x^2}{2}\right|_{0}^{1} + \left.\left(2x - \dfrac{x^2}{2}\right)\right|_{1}^{1.2} = 0.68.$

       (b) $P(0.5 < X < 1) = \int_{0.5}^{1} x\, dx = \left.\dfrac{x^2}{2}\right|_{0.5}^{1} = 0.375$

9.   (a) $P(0 < X < 1) = \int_{0}^{1} \dfrac{2(x+2)}{5} dx = \left.\dfrac{(x+2)^2}{5}\right|_{0}^{1} = 1.$

       (b) $P(1/4 < X < 1/2) = \int_{1/4}^{1/2} \dfrac{2(x+2)}{5} dx = \left.\dfrac{(x+2)^2}{5}\right|_{1/4}^{1/2}$
           $= 19/80.$

11. We can select x defective sets from 2 and 3 − x good sets from 5 in $\binom{2}{x}\binom{5}{3-x}$ ways.

A random selection of 3 from 7 sets can be made in $\binom{7}{3}$ ways. Therefore,

$$f(x) = \frac{\binom{2}{x}\binom{5}{3-x}}{\binom{7}{3}} = x = 0, 1, 2.$$

In tabular form,

x	0	1	2
f(x)	2/7	4/7	1/7

As a probability histogram

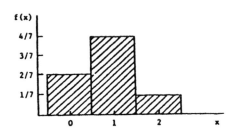

13.
$$F(x) = \begin{cases} 0 & \text{for} & x < 0 \\ 0.41 & \text{for} & 0 \le x < 1 \\ 0.78 & \text{for} & 1 \le x < 2 \\ 0.94 & \text{for} & 2 \le x < 3 \\ 0.99 & \text{for} & 3 \le x < 4 \\ 1 & \text{for} & x \ge 4 \end{cases}$$

15.
$$F(x) = \begin{cases} 0 & \text{for} & x < 0 \\ 2/7 & \text{for} & 0 \le x < 1 \\ 6/7 & \text{for} & 1 \le x < 2 \\ 1 & \text{for} & x \ge 2 \end{cases}$$

(a) $P(X = 1) = P(x \le 1) - P(X \le 0) = 6/7 - 2/7 = 4/7.$
(b) $P(0 < X \le 2) = P(X \le 2) - P(X \le 0) = 1 - 2/7 = 5/7.$

17. (a) Area $= \int_1^3 1/2\,dx = x/2\big|_1^3 = 1.$

(b) $P(2 < x < 2.5) = \int_2^{2.5} 1/2\,dx = x/2\big|_2^{2.5} = 1/4.$

(c) $P(x \le 1.6) = \int_1^{1.6} 1/2\,dx = x/2\big|_1^{1.6} = 0.3.$

19. $F(x) = \int_1^x 1/2\, dt = t/2\big|_1^x = (x-1)/2.$

$P(2 < X < 2.5) = F(2.5) - F(2) = 1.5/2 - 1/2 = 1/4.$

21. (a) $1 = k\int_0^1 \sqrt{x}\, dx = \dfrac{2k}{3} x^{3/2}\big|_0^1 = 2k/3.$ Therefore $k = 3/2.$

(b) $F(x) = \dfrac{3}{2}\int_0^x \sqrt{t}\, dt = t^{3/2}\big|_0^x = x^{3/2}.$

$P(0.3 < X < 0.6) = F(0.6) - F(0.3) = (0.6)^{3/2} - (0.3)^{3/2}$
$= 0.3004$

23.
$$F(x) = \begin{cases} 0 & \text{for} & w < -3 \\ 1/27 & \text{for} & -3 \le w < 3 \\ 7/27 & \text{for} & -1 \le w < 1 \\ 19/27 & \text{for} & 1 \le w < 3 \\ 1 & \text{for} & w \ge 3. \end{cases}$$

(a) $P(W > 0) = 1 - P(W \le 0) = 1 - 7/27 = 20/27.$

(b) $P(-1 \le W < 3) = P(W \le 2) - P(W \le -2) = 19/27 - 1/27 = 2/3.$

25. Let T be the total value of the three coins. Let D and N stand for a dime and nickel, respectively. Since we are selecting without replacement, the sample space contains elements for which t = 20, 25, and 30 cents corresponding to the selection of 2 nickels and 1 dime, 1 nickel and 2 dimes, and 3 dimes. Therefore,

$$P(T = 20) = \frac{\binom{2}{2}\binom{4}{1}}{\binom{6}{3}} = \frac{1}{5},$$

$$P(T = 25) = \frac{\binom{2}{1}\binom{4}{2}}{\binom{6}{3}} = \frac{3}{5},$$

$$P(T = 30) = \frac{\binom{4}{3}}{\binom{6}{3}} = \frac{1}{5},$$

and the probability distribution in tabular form is

t	20	25	30
P(T = t)	1/5	3/5	1/5

As a probability histogram

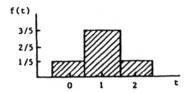

Section 3.4 Joint Probability Distributions

1.   (a) $\sum_{x=1}^{3}\sum_{y=1}^{3} f(x, y) = c\sum_{x=1}^{3}\sum_{y=1}^{3} xy = 36c = 1$. Hence $c = 1/36$.

     b) $\sum_{x}\sum_{y} f(x, y) = c\sum_{x}\sum_{y}|x - y| = 15c = 1$. Hence $c = 1/15$.

3.   (a)   We can select x oranges from 3, y apples from 2, and $4 - x - y$ bananas from 3 in

$\binom{3}{x}\binom{2}{y}\binom{3}{4-x-y}$ ways. A random selection of 4 pieces of fruit can be made in $\binom{8}{4}$

ways. Therefore,

$$f(x, y) = \frac{\binom{3}{x}\binom{2}{y}\binom{3}{4-x-y}}{\binom{8}{4}}, x = 0, 1, 2, 3; y = 0, 1, 2; 1 \le x + y \le 4.$$

     (b) $P[(X, Y) \varepsilon A] = P(X + Y \le 2)$
                           $= f(1, 0) + f(2, 0) + f(0, 1) + f(1, 1) + f(0, 2)$
                           $= 3/70 + 9/70 + 2/70 + 18/70 + 3/70 = 1/2.$

5.   (a) $P(X + Y \le 1/2) = \int_{0}^{1/2}\int_{0}^{1/2-y} 24xy\, dxdy$

$$= 12\int_{0}^{1/2}\left(\frac{1}{2} - y\right)^{2} y\, dy$$

$$= 1/16.$$

     (b) $g(x) = \int_{0}^{1-x} 24xy\, dy = 12x(1 - x)^{2}, 0 \le x \le 11.$

$f(y \mid x) = \dfrac{24xy}{12x(1-x)^{2}} = \dfrac{2y}{(1-x)^{2}}, 0 \le y \le 1 - x.$ Therefore

$P(Y < 1/8 \mid X = 3/4) = 32\int_{0}^{1/8} y\, dy = 1/4.$

7.   (a) $P(0 \le x \le 1/2,\ 1/4 \le Y \le 1/2) = \int_{0}^{1/2} \int_{1/4}^{1/2} 4xy\, dy\, dx$

$$= 3/8 \int_{0}^{1/2} x\, dx = 3/64$$

    (b) $P(X < Y) = \int_{0}^{1} \int_{0}^{y} 4xy\, dx\, dy = 2\int_{0}^{1} y^3 dy = 1/2$

9. $P(X + Y > 1/2) = 1 - P(X + Y < 1/2)$

$$= 1 - \int_{0}^{1/4} \int_{0}^{y} \frac{1}{y}\, dx\, dy - \int_{1/4}^{1/2} \int_{0}^{1/2-y} \frac{1}{y}\, dx\, dy$$

$$= 1 - \int_{0}^{1/4} dy - \int_{1/4}^{1/2} \frac{1}{y}\left(\frac{1}{2} - y\right) dy = 0.6534.$$

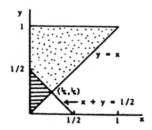

11.   (a) $g(x) = 2\int_{x}^{1} dy = 2(1 - x),\ 0 < x < 1;$

$h(y) = 2\int_{0}^{y} dx = 2y,\ 0 < y < 1.$

Since $f(x, y) \ne g(x)h(y)$, X and Y are not independent.

    (b) $f(x \mid y) = f(x, y)/h(y) = 1/y,\ 0 < x < y.$ Therefore

$P(1/4 < X < 1/2 \mid Y = 3/4) = \dfrac{4}{3} \int_{1/4}^{1/2} dx = 1/3.$

13.   (a)

x	1	2	3
g(x)	.10	.35	.55

    (b)

y	1	2	3
h(y)	.20	.50	.30

    (c) $P(Y = 3 \mid X = 2) = \dfrac{0.2}{0.05 + 0.10 + 0.20} = 0.5714.$

14

15. (a) Let X = number of 4's and Y = number of 5's. The sample space consists of 36 elements each with probability 1/36 of the form (m, n) where m is the outcome of the first roll of the die and n is the value obtained on the second roll. The joint probability distribution f(x, y) is defined for x = 0, 1, 2 and y = 0, 1, 2 with $0 \le x + y \le 2$. To find f(0, 1), for example, consider the event A of obtaining zero 4's and one 5 in the 2 rolls. Then A = {(1, 5), (2, 5), (3, 5), (6, 5), (5, 1), (5, 2), (5, 3), (5, 6)}, and f(0, 1) = 8/36. In a like manner we find f(0, 0) = 16/36, f(0, 2) = 1/36, f(1, 0) = 8/36, f(2, 0) = 1/36, f(1, 1) = 2/36.

(b) $P[(X, Y) \varepsilon A] = P(2X + y < 3) = f(0, 0) + f(0, 1) + f(0, 2) + f(1, 0)$
$= 16/36 + 8/36 + 1/36 + 8/36 = 11/12.$

17. (a) If (x, y) represents the selection of x kings and y jacks in 3 draws, then we must have x = 0, 1, 2, 3; y = 0, 1, 2, 3; and $0 \le x + y \le 3$. Therefore, (1, 2) represents the selection of 1 king and 2 jacks which will occur with probability

$$f(1, 2) = \frac{\binom{4}{1}\binom{4}{2}}{\binom{12}{3}} = \frac{6}{55}.$$

Proceeding in a similar fashion for the other possibilities, we arrive at the following joint probability distribution:

f(x, y)		x = 0	1	2	3
y	0	1/55	6/55	6/55	1/55
	1	6/55	16/55	6/55	
	2	6/55	6/55		
	3	1/55			

(b) $P[(X, Y) \varepsilon A] = P(X + Y \ge 2) = 1 - P(X + Y < 2)$
$= 1 - 1/55 - 6/55 - 6/55 = 42/55.$

19. $f(y \mid x) = f(x, y)/g(x)$. Now,

$$g(x) = \frac{1}{8}\int_2^4 (6 - x - y)dy = (3 - x)/4,\ 0 < x < 2.$$ Therefore

$$f(y \mid x) = \frac{(6 - x - y)}{2(3 - x)},\ 2 < y < 4,$$

and

$$P(1 < Y < 3 \mid X = 2) = \frac{1}{2}\int_2^3 (4 - y)dy = 3/4.$$

21. X and Y are independent since f(x, y) = g(x)h(y) for akk x and y.

23.   (a)

$$1 = k \int_0^1 \int_0^1 \int_0^2 xy^2 z\,dz\,dy\,dx = 2k \int_0^1 \int_0^1 y^2 x\,dy\,dx = \frac{2k}{3} \int_0^1 x\,dx = k/3,$$

Therefore $k = 3$.

(b) $P(X < 1/4, Y > 1/2, 1 < Z < 2)$

$$= \int_0^{1/4} \int_{1/2}^1 \int_1^2 xy^2 z\,dz\,dy\,dx = \frac{9}{2} \int_0^{1/4} \int_{1/2}^1 y^2 x\,dy\,dx = \frac{21}{16} \int_0^{1/4} x\,dx = 21/512.$$

25. $\displaystyle g(x) = k \int_{30}^{50} (x^2 + y^2)\,dy = k \left[x^2 y + \frac{y^3}{3} \right]_{30}^{50}$

$$= k \left[50x^2 + \frac{125.00}{3} - 30x^2 - \frac{27.00}{3} \right]$$

$$= k \left[20x^2 + \frac{98,000}{3} \right]$$

$$h(y) = k \left[20y^2 + \frac{98,000}{3} \right]$$

$f(x, y) \neq g(x)\,h(y)$; X and Y are not independent.

Chapter 4
Mathematical Expectation

Section 4.1 Mean of a Random Variable

1. $E[X] = \dfrac{1}{\pi a^2} \displaystyle\int_{-a}^{a} \int_{-\sqrt{a^2-y^2}}^{\sqrt{a^2-y^2}} x\,dx\,dy = \dfrac{1}{\pi a^2} \int_{-a}^{a}\left[\left(\dfrac{a^2-y^2}{2}\right) - \left(\dfrac{a^2-y^2}{2}\right)\right]dy = 0.$

    $E[X] = 0.$

3. $\mu = E(T) = (20)(1/5) + (25)(3/5) + (30)(1/5) = 25c.$

5. $\mu = E(X) = (0)(0.41) + (1)(0.37) + (2)(0.16) + (3)(0.05) + (4)(0.01)$
    $= 0.88.$

7. Expected gain $= E(X) = (4000)(0.3) + (-1000)(0.7) = \$500.$

9. Let c = amount to play the game, Y = amount won.

y	5–c	3–c	–c
f(y)	2/13	2/13	9/13

    $E(Y) = (5 - c)(2/13) + (3 - c)(2/13) + (-c)(9/13) = 0.$
    Solving, 13c = 16 or c = \$1.23.

11. Insurance for \$200,000.

Loss	Prob.	Expected Claim
100%	0.002	\$400.00
50%	0.010	\$1000.00
25%	0.100	$\underline{\$5000.00}$
		\$6400.00

    Premium = \$6400.00 + \$500.00 profit = \$6900.00

13. $E(X) = \dfrac{4}{\pi} \displaystyle\int_{0}^{1} \dfrac{x}{1+x^2}dx = \dfrac{\ln 4}{\pi}.$

15. $E(X) = \displaystyle\int_{0}^{1} x^2 dx + \int_{1}^{2} x(2-x)dx = 1.$ Therefore, the average number of hours per year is
    $(1)(100) = 100.$

17.
x	–3	6	9
f(x)	1/6	1/2	1/3
g(x)	25	169	361

    $\mu_{g(x)} = E[(2X + 1)^2] = (25)(1/6) + (169)(1/2) + (361)(1/3) = 209.$

19. Let $g(X) = 1200X - 50X^2$ be the amount spent.

x	0	1	2	3
f(x)	1/10	3/10	2/5	1/5
g(x)	0	1150	2200	3150

$$\mu_{g(X)} = E(1200X - 50X^2)$$
$$= (0)(1/10) + (1150)(3/10) + (2200)(2/5) + (3150)(1/5)$$
$$= \$1855.$$

21. $E[X^2] = \int_0^1 2x^2(1-x)dx = \frac{1}{6}$ Therefore the average profit per new automobile is

$(1/6)(\$5000.00) = \$833.33$

23. (a) $E[g(X, Y)] = E(XY^2) = \sum_x \sum_y xy^2 f(x, y) = (2)(1)^2(0.10)$

$+ (2)(3)^2(0.20) + \cdots + (4)(5)^2(0.15) = 35.2$

(b) $\mu_X = E(X) = (2)(0.40) + (4)(0.60) = 3.20,$
$\mu_Y = E(Y) = (1)(0.25) + (3)(0.50) + (5)(0.25) = 3.00.$

25. From Exercise 17(a) on page 25 of this manual.

$$\mu_{X+Y} = E(X + Y) = \sum_{x=0}^{3} \sum_{y=0}^{3} (x + y)f(x, y)$$
$$= (0 + 0)(1/55) + (1 + 0)(6/55) + \cdots + (0 + 3)(1/55) = 2.$$

Section 4.2 Variance and Covariance

1.

x	−$1000	$4000
f(x)	0.7	0.3

$\mu = \$500.$

$$\sigma^2 = E[X - \mu]^2 = \sum (x - \mu)^2 f(x)$$
$$= (-\$1500.)^2(0.7) + (\$3500.)^2(0.3)$$
$$= \$5,250,000.$$

3. $\mu = (2)(0.01) + (3)(0.25) + (4)(0.4) + (5)(0.3) + (6)(0.04) = 4.11;$
$E(X^2) = (4)(0.01) + (9)(0.25) + (16)(0.4) + (25)(0.3) + (36)(0.04) = 17.63;$
$\sigma^2 = 17.63 - 4.11^2 = 0.74.$

5. From Exercise 12 on page 32 of this manual $\mu = 1/3.$

$E(X^2) = \int_0^1 2x^2(1-x)dx = 1/6; \sigma^2 = 1/6 - (1/3)^2 = 1/18.$

Variance in terms of profit is $1/18(\$5000.00)^2 = \$1,388,888.89.$

7. Previously we found $\mu = 1$. Now,

$$E(X^2) = \int_0^1 x^3 dx + \int_1^2 x^2(2-x)dx = 7/6$$

and hence

$$\sigma^2 = E(X^2) - \mu^2 = 7/6 - 1 = 1/6.$$

9. Previously we found $\mu_{g(X)} = E[(2x+1)^2] = 209$. Hence,

$$\begin{aligned}\sigma^2_{g(X)} &= \sum_x [(2x+1)^2 - 209]^2 f(x)\\
&= (25-209)^2(1/6) + (169-209)^2(1/2) + (361-209)^2(1/3)\\
&= 14{,}444.\end{aligned}$$

Therefore, $\sigma_{g(X)} = 118.9$.

11. $$\mu_Y = E(3X-2) = \frac{1}{4}\int_0^\infty (3x-2)e^{-x/4}dx = 10,$$

$$\sigma^2_Y = E\{[(3X-2)-10]^2\} = \frac{9}{4}\int_0^\infty (x-4)^2 e^{-x/4}dx = 144.$$

13. $\sigma_{xy} = E[XY] - \mu_x\mu_y = \mu_x = \sum xg(x) = 2.45 \quad \mu_y = \sum xh(y) = 2.10$

$E(XY) = \sum\sum xy f(x,y) = (1)(0.05) + (2)(0.05) + (3)(0.10) + (2)(0.05) +$
$(4)(0.10) + (6)(0.35) + (3)(0) + (6)(0.20) + (9)(0.10) = 5.15$;
$\sigma_{xy} = 5.150 - 5.145 = 0.005.$

15. $$f(x,y) = \begin{cases} \frac{2}{3}(x+2y) & 0 \le x \le 1; 0 \le y \le 1;\\ 3 & \text{elsewhere}\end{cases}$$

$$g(x) = \frac{2}{3}\int_0^1 (x+2y)dy = \frac{2}{3}(x+1);$$

$$\mu_x = \frac{2}{3}\int_0^1 x(x+1)dx = \frac{5}{9};$$

$$h(y) = \frac{2}{3}\int_0^1 (x+2y)dx = \frac{2}{3}\left(\frac{1}{2}+2y\right);$$

$$\mu_y = \frac{2}{3}\int_0^1 y\left(\frac{1}{2}+2y\right)dy = \frac{11}{18};$$

$$E[XY] = \frac{2}{3}\int_0^1\int_0^1 xy(x+2y)dydx = \frac{1}{3};$$

$$\sigma_{xy} = E[XY] - \mu_x\mu_y = 0.3333 - \left(\frac{5}{9}\right)\left(\frac{11}{18}\right) = -0.0062.$$

Section 4.4 Chebyshev's Theorem

1. Previously we found $\mu = 4.11$ and $\sigma^2 = 0.74$. Therefore, $\mu_{g(X)} = E(3X - 2) = 3\mu - 2 = (3)(4.11) - 2 = 10.33$ and $\sigma^2_{g(X)} = 9\sigma^2 = 6.66$.

3. Let X = number of cartons sold and Y = profit. We can write
$$Y = 1.65X + 0.90(5 - X) - 6$$
$$= 0.75X - 1.50.$$
Now,
$$E(X) = (0)(1/15) + (1)(2/15) + (2)(2/15) + (3)(3/15) + (4)(4/15) + (5)(3/15)$$
$$= 46/15$$
and
$$E(Y) = 0.75 \ E(X) - 1.50 = (0.75)(46/15) - 1.50 = \$0.80.$$

5. $E[X] = (-3)(1/6) + (6)(1/2) + (9)(1/3) = 11/2$.
$E[X]^2 = (9)(1/6) + (36)(1/2) + (81)(1/3) = 93/2$.
$E[(2X + 1)^2] = 4E[X^2] + 4E[X] + 1 = (4)(93/2) + (4)(11/2) + 1 = 209$.

7. The equations $E[(X - 1)^2] = 10$ and $E[(X - 2)^2] = 6$ may be written in the form
$$E(X^2) - 2E(X) = 9$$
$$E(X^2) - 4E(X) = 2.$$
Solving simultaneously, we obtain $E(X) = 7/2$, $E(X^2) = 16$.
Hence, $\mu = 7/2$ and $\sigma^2 = 16 - 49/4 = 15/4$.

9. $E(2XY^2 - X^2Y) = 2E(XY^2) - E(X^2Y)$. Now,

$$E(XY^2) = \sum_{x=0}^{2}\sum_{y=0}^{2} xy^2 f(x, y) = (1)(1)^2(3/14) = 3/14$$

and

$$E(X^2Y) = \sum_{x=0}^{2}\sum_{y=0}^{2} x^2 y \ f(x, y) = (1)^2(1)(3/14) = 3/14.$$

Therefore,
$$E(2XY^2 - X^2Y) = (2)(3/14) - (3/14) = 3/14.$$

11. $\mu = 900$ hours $\qquad \sigma = 50$ hours

$P[x \le 700]$ using Chebyshev's theorem.
$\mu - k\sigma = 700 \qquad k = 4$
$P(\mu - 4\sigma \le x \le \mu + 4\sigma) \ge .9375$
$P(700 \le x \le 1100) \ge .9375$
$P[X \le 700] < .03125$

13. $n = 500$ $\mu = 4.5$ $\sigma = 2.8723$

$\mu = k(\sigma/\sqrt{500}) = 5$

$k = \dfrac{5 - 4.5}{2.8723/\sqrt{500}} = \dfrac{.5}{.1284} = 3.8924$

$P[4 \leq \bar{x} \leq 5] \geq 1 - \dfrac{1}{k^2} = .9340$

15. $\sigma_Z^2 = \sigma_{-2X+4Y-3}^2 = \sigma_{-2X+4Y}^2 = 4\sigma_X^2 + 16\sigma_Y^2 - 16\sigma_{XY}$
$= (4)(5) + (16)(3) - (16)(1) = 52.$

17. (a) $P(|X - 10| \geq 3) = 1 - P(|X - 10| < 3)$
$= 1 - P(-3 < X - 10 < 3) = 1 - P(7 < X < 13)$
$= 1 - P[10 - (2)(3/2) < X < 10 + (2)(3/2)] \leq 4/9.$

(b) $P(|X - 10| < 3) = 1 - P(|X - 10| \geq 3) \geq 1 - 4/9 = 5/9.$

(c) $P(5 < X < 15) = P[10 - (5/2)(2) < X < 10 + (5/2)(2)] \geq 21/25.$

(d) Since $P(|X - 10| \geq c) \leq 0.04$, then $P(|X - 10| < c) \geq 0.96$.
However, $P(|X - 10| < c) = P(-c < X - 10 < c)$
$= P(10 - c < X < 10 + c) \geq 0.96$. Let $c = k\sigma = 2k$, and we have
$1 - 1/k^2 = 1 - (2/c)^2 = 0.96$. Solving, $c = 10.$

19. (a) $E(X + Y) = E(X) + E(Y) = 3.5 + 3.5 = 7.0.$
(b) $E(X - Y) = E(X) - E(Y) = 3.5 - 3.5 = 0.$
(c) $E(XY) = E(X)E(Y) = (3.5)(3.5) = 12.25.$

21. $E[g(X, Y)] = E(X/Y^2 + X^2Y) = E(X/Y^3) + E(X^2Y).$

$E[X/Y^3] = \int\limits_1^2\int\limits_0^1 \dfrac{2x(x + 2y)}{7y^3}dxdy = \dfrac{2}{7}\int\limits_1^2\left(\dfrac{1}{3y^3} + \dfrac{1}{y^2}\right)dy = \dfrac{15}{84};$

$E[X^2Y] = \int\limits_1^2\int\limits_0^1 \dfrac{2x^2y(x + 2y)}{7}dxdy = \dfrac{2}{7}\int\limits_1^2 y\left(\dfrac{1}{4} + \dfrac{2y}{3}\right)dy = \dfrac{139}{252};$

$E[X/Y^3 + X^2Y] = \dfrac{15}{84} + \dfrac{139}{253} = \dfrac{46}{63}.$

23. Chebychev's Theorem $P[(\mu - k\sigma) \leq X \leq (\mu + k\sigma)] > (1 - 1/k^2);$
$k = 2$ $P[(2.5 - 2\sigma) \leq X \leq (2.5 + 2\sigma)] = 0.95 \geq 0.75;$
$k = 3$ $P[(2.5 - 3\sigma) \leq X \leq (2.5 + 3\sigma)] = 0.997 \geq 0.89;$

Chapter 5
Some Discrete Probability Distributions

Section 5.3 Binomial and Multinomial Distributions

1.   Uniform distribution: $f(x) = 1/10$, $x = 1, 2, \ldots, 10$.

$$P(x < 4) = \sum_{x=1}^{3} f(x) = 3/10.$$

3. $\mu = \sum_{x=1}^{10} x/10 = 5.5$; $\sigma^2 = \sum_{x=1}^{10}(x - 5.5)^2/10 = 8.25$

5.   (a) $P(X \geq 10) = 1. - 0.9520 = 0.0480$
      (b) $P(X \leq 4) = 0.2375$
      (c) $P(X = 5 \mid p = 0.3) = 0.1789$ $p = 0.30$ is reasonable

7. $p = 0.70$,
      (a) For $n = 10$, $P[X < 5] = P[X \leq 4] = 0.0474$.
      (b) For $n = 20$, $P[X < 10] = P[X \leq 9] = 0.0171$.

9.   For $n = 15$ and $p = 0.25$, we have

      (a) $P(3 \leq X \leq 6) = \sum_{x=0}^{6} b(x; 15, 0.25) - \sum_{x=0}^{2} b(x; 15, 0.25)$
           $= 0.9434 - 0.2361 = 0.7073.$

      (b) $P(x < 4) = \sum_{x=0}^{3} b(x; 15, 0.25) = 0.4613.$

      (c) $P(X > 5) = 1 - P(X \leq 5) = 1 - \sum_{x=0}^{5} b(x; 15, 0.25)$
           $= 1 - 0.8516 = 0.1484.$

11.   From Table A.1 with $n = 7$ and $p = 0.9$, we have
      $$P(X = 5) = \sum_{x=0}^{5} b(x; 7, 0.9) - \sum_{x=0}^{4} b(x; 7, 0.9)$$
      $$= 0.1497 - 0.0257 = 0.1240.$$

13.   From Table A. 1, with $n = 5$ and $p = 0.7$, we have
      $$P(X \geq 3) = 1 - P(X \leq 2) = 1 - \sum_{x=0}^{2} b(x; 5, 0.7)$$
      $$= 1 - 0.1631 = 0.8369.$$

15. $p = 0.4$, $n = 5$;

(a) $P[X = 0] = 0.0778$.
(b) $P[X < 2] = P[X \le 1] = 0.3370$
(c) $P[X > 3] = 1 - P[X \le 3] = 1 - 0.9130 = 0.0870$.

17. $\mu = np = (5)(0.7) = 3.5$, $\sigma^2 = npq = (5)(0.7)(0.3) = 1.05$, $\sigma = 1.025$. Then $\mu + 2\sigma = 3.5 \pm (2)(1.025) = 3.5 \pm 2.050$ or from 1.45 to 5.55. Therefore, at least 3/4 of the time when 5 people are selected at random, anywhere from 2 to 5 are of the opinion that tranquilizers do not cure but only cover up the real problem.

19. $P[\text{green}] = .35$ $x_1 =$ Number of times encounters green light
     $P[\text{yellow}] = .05$ $x_2 =$ Number of times encounters yellow light
     $P[\text{red}] = .60$ $x_3 =$ Number of times encounters red light

$$f(x_1, x_2, x_3) = \binom{n}{x_1 x_2 x_3} \qquad .35^{x_1}\, .05^{x_2}\, .60^{x_3}$$

21.   Using the multinomial distribution the required probability is
$$\binom{7}{0,0,1,4,2}(0.02)(0.82)^4(0.1)^2 = 0.0095.$$

23.   Using the multinomial distribution, we have
$$\binom{9}{3,3,1,2}(0.4)^3(0.2)^3(0.3)(0.1)^2 = 0.0077.$$

25. $p = 0.10$; probability of a defective; $n = 20$
$P[X \le 3] = 0.8670$

27. $p = 0.90$ $n = 20$
(a) $P[x = 18] = P[X \le 18] - P[X \le 17] = 0.6083 - 0.3231 = 0.2852$
(b) $P[x \ge 15] = 1 - P(X \le 14) = 1. - 0.0113 = 0.9887$
(c) $P[X \le 18] = 0.6083$

Section 5.4 Hypergeometric Distribution

1.   Using the hypergeometric distribution, we get

(a) $\dfrac{\binom{12}{2}\binom{40}{5}}{\binom{52}{7}} = 0.3246$ (b) $1 - \dfrac{\binom{48}{7}}{\binom{52}{7}} = 0.4496$

3.   Using the hypergeometric distribution, we get

$$h(2; 9, 6, 4) = \frac{\binom{4}{2}\binom{5}{4}}{\binom{9}{6}} = 5/14.$$

5. $h(x; 6, 3, 4) = \dfrac{\dbinom{4}{x}\dbinom{2}{3-x}}{\dbinom{6}{3}}$, for x = 1, 2, 3.

$P(2 \le X \le 3) = h(2; 6, 3, 4) + h(3; 6, 3, 4) = 4/5.$

7. $P(X \le 2) = \displaystyle\sum_{x=0}^{2} h(x; 50, 5, 10) = 0.9517.$

9. (a) $P(X = 0) = b(0; 3, 3/25) = 0.6815.$

(b) $P(1 \le X \le 3) = \displaystyle\sum_{x=1}^{3} b(x; 3, 1/25) = 0.1153.$

11. By Theorem 5.3, $\mu = (13)(13)/52 = 3.25$, $\sigma^2 = (39/51)(13)(1/4) \times (3/4) = 1.864$, $\sigma = 1.365$. At least 75% of the time the number of hearts lay between $\mu \pm 2\sigma = 3.25 \pm (2)(1.365)$ or from 0.52 to 5.98.

13. Using the binomial approximation of the hypergeometric with p = 0.5 the probability is

$$1 - \sum_{x=0}^{2} b(x; 10, 0.5) = 0.9453.$$

15. Using the binomial approximation of the hypergeometric distribution with p = 0.7 the probability is

$$\sum_{x=10}^{13} b(x; 18, 0.7) = .6077$$

17. (a) The extension of the hypergeometric distribution gives a probability of

$$\dfrac{\dbinom{2}{1}\dbinom{3}{1}\dbinom{5}{1}\dbinom{2}{1}}{\dbinom{12}{4}} = 4/33.$$

(b) Using the extension of the hypergeometric distribution, we have

$$\dfrac{\dbinom{2}{1}\dbinom{3}{1}\dbinom{2}{2}}{\dbinom{12}{4}} + \dfrac{\dbinom{2}{2}\dbinom{3}{1}\dbinom{2}{1}}{\dbinom{12}{4}} + \dfrac{\dbinom{2}{1}\dbinom{3}{2}\dbinom{2}{1}}{\dbinom{12}{4}} = 8/165.$$

19. $\dfrac{\dbinom{10}{5}\dbinom{15}{10}}{\dbinom{25}{15}} = 0.2315$

21. (a) $\dfrac{\dbinom{3}{0}\dbinom{17}{5}}{\dbinom{20}{5}} = 0.3991$ (b) $\dfrac{\dbinom{3}{2}\dbinom{17}{3}}{\dbinom{20}{5}} = 0.1316$

Section 5.6 Poisson Distribution and the Poisson Process

1. Using the negative binomial distribution, the required probability is

$$b^*(10; 5, 0.3) = \binom{9}{4}(0.3)^5(0.7)^5 = 0.0515$$

3. (a) $P(X > 5) = \sum\limits_{x=6}^{\infty} p(x; 5) = 1 - \sum\limits_{x=0}^{5} p(x; 5) = 0.3840.$

   (b) $P(X = 0) = p(0; 5) = 0.0067.$

5. Probability all coins turn up the same is 1/4. Using the geometric distribution with p = 3/4 and q = 1/4, we have

$$P(X < 4) = \sum_{x=1}^{3} g(x; 3/4) = \sum_{x=1}^{3}(3/4)(1/4)^{x-1} = 63/64.$$

7. Using the geometric distribution
   (a) $P(X = 3) = g(3; 0.7) = (0.7)(0.3)^2 = 0.0630.$

   (b) $P(X < 4) = \sum\limits_{x=1}^{3} g(x; 0.7) = \sum\limits_{x=1}^{3}(0.7)(0.3)^{x-1} = 0.9730.$

9. (a) $P(X \geq 4) = \sum\limits_{x=4}^{3} p(x; 2) = 1 - \sum\limits_{x=0}^{3} p(x; 2) = 0.1429.$

   (b) $P(X = 0) = p(0; 2) = 0.1353.$

11. (a) Using the negative binomial distribution, we obtain

   $$b^*(6; 4, 0.8) = \binom{5}{3}(0.8)^4(*0.2)^2 = 0.1638.$$

   (b) From the geometric distribution, we have
   $g(3; 0.8) = (0.8)(0.2)^2 = 0.032.$

13. (a) Using the Poisson distribution with $\mu = 5$, we find from Table A.2 that

$$P(X > 5) = \sum_{x=6}^{\infty} p(x; 5) = 1 - \sum_{x=0}^{5} p(x; 5) = 0.3840.$$

(b) Using the binomial distribution with p = 0.384, we get

$$b(3; 4, 0.384) = \binom{4}{3}(0.384)^3(0.616) = 0.1395.$$

(c) Using the geometric distribution with p = 0.384, we have
$$g(5; 0.384) = (0.384)(0.616)^4 = 0.0553.$$

15. $\mu = np = (10,000)(0.001) = 10.$

$$P(6 \le X \le 8) = \sum_{x=6}^{8} b(x; 10,000, 0.001) \cong \sum_{x=6}^{8} p(x; 10)$$

$$= \sum_{x=0}^{8} p(x; 10) - \sum_{x=0}^{5} p(x; 10) = 0.2657.$$

17. (a) $\mu = (2000)(0.002) = 4;\ \sigma^2 = 4.$
    (b) For k = 2 we have $\mu \pm 2\sigma = 4 \pm 4$ or from 0 to 8.

19. (a) $P[X \le 3] | \lambda = 5] = 0.2650$
    (b) $P[X > 1] | \lambda = 5] = 1. - 0.0404 = 0.9596$

21. (a) $P[X > 10 | \lambda t = 14] = 1. - 0.1757 = 0.8243$
    (b) $\lambda t = 14$

23. $\mu = np = (2000)(0.002) = 4$

Chapter 6
Some Continuous Probability Distributions

Section 6.4 Applications of the Normal Distribution

1. (a) Area = 0.9236.
    (b) Area = $1 - 0.1867 = 0.8133$.
    (c) Area = $0.2578 - 0.0154 = 0.2424$.
    (d) Area = 0.0823.
    (e) Area = $1 - 0.9750 = 0.0250$.
    (f) Area = $0.9591 - 0.3156 = 0.6435$.

3. (a) From Table A.3, $k = -1.72$.
    (b) Since $P(Z > k) = 0.2946$, then $P(Z < k) = 0.7054$. From Table A.3 we find $k = 0.54$.
    (c) The area to the left of $z = 0.83$ is found from Table A.3 to be 0.1762. Therefore, the total area to the left of k is $0.1762 + 0.7235 = 0.8997$, and hence $k = 1.28$.

5. (a) $z = (15 - 18)/2.5 = -1.2$; $P(X < 15) = P(Z < -1.2) = 0.1151$.
    (b) $z = -0.76$, $k = (2.5)(-0.76) + 18 = 16.1$.
    (c) $z = 0.91$, $k = (2.5)(0.91) + 18 = 20.275$.
    (d) $z_1 = (17 - 18)/2.5 = -0.4$, $z_2 = (21 - 18)/2.5 = 1.2$;
$$P(17 < X < 21) = P(-0.4 < Z < 1.2)$$
$$= 0.8849 - 0.3446$$
$$= 0.5403.$$

7. (a) $z = (32 - 40)/6.3 = -1.27$; $P(X > 32) = P(Z > -1.27) = 1 - 0.1020 = 0.8980$.
    (b) $z = (28 - 40)/6.3 = -1.90$; $P(X < 28) = P(Z < -1.90) = 0.0287$.
    (c) $z_1 = (37 - 40)/6.3 = -0.48$, $z_2 = (49 - 40)/6.3 = 1.43$;
$P(37 < X < 49) = P(-0.48 < Z < 1.43) = 0.9236 - 0.3156 = 0.6080$.

9. (a) $z = (224 - 200)/15 = 1.6$. Fraction of the cups containing more than 224 milliliters is $P(Z > 1.6) = 0.0548$.
    (b) $z_1 = (191 - 200)/15 = -0.6$, $z_2 = (209 - 200)/15 = 0.6$;
$P(191 < X < 209) = P(-0.6 < Z < 0.6) = 0.7257 - 0.2743 = 0.4514$.
    (c) $z = (230 - 200)/15 = 2.0$; $P(X > 230] = P(Z > 2.0] = 0.0228$.
Therefore, $(1000)(0.0228) = 22.8$ or approximately 23 cups will overflow.
    (d) $z = -0.67$, $x = (15)(-0.67) + 200 = 189.95$ milliliters.

11. (a) $z = (30 - 24)/3.8 = 1.58$; $P(X > 30) = P(Z > 1.58) = 0.0571$.
    (b) $z = (15 - 24)/3.8 = -2.37$; $P(X > 15) = P(Z > -2.37) = 0.9911$. He is late 99.11% of the time.
    (c) $z = (25 - 24)/3.8 = 0.26$; $P(X > 25) = P(Z > 0.26) = 0.3974$.
    (d) $z = 1.04$, $x = (3.8)(1.04) + 24 = 27.952$ minutes.
    (e) Using the binomial distribution with $p = 0.0571$, we get
$$b(2; 3, 0.0571) = \binom{3}{2}(0.0571)^2(0.9429) = 0.0092.$$

13. $z = -1.88$, $x = (2)(-1.88) + 10 = 6.24$ years.

15. $\mu = \$15.90$ $\sigma = \$1.50$

   (a) 51%., since

   $$P[13.75 < X < 16.22] = P\left[\frac{13.745 - 15.9}{1.5} < Z < \frac{16.225 - 15.9}{1.5}\right]$$
   $$= P[-1.437 < Z < 0.217] = 0.5871 - 0.0749 = 0.5122$$

   (b) $18.36, since $P[Z > 1.645] = 0.05$; $x = z\sigma + \mu$;
   $X = (1.645)(1.50) + 15.90 + .005 = 18.37$

17. (a) $z = (10,175 - 10,000)/100 = 1.75$. Proportion of components exceeding 10,150 kilograms in tensile strength
   $= P(X > 10,175) = P(Z > 1.75) = 0.0401$.
   (b) $z_1 = (9,775 - 10,000)/100 = -2.25$, $z_2 = (10,225 - 10,000)/100 = 2.25$.
   Proportion of components scrapped
   $= P(X < 9,775) + P(X > 10,225) = P(Z < -2.25) + P(Z > 2.25)$
   $= 2P(Z < -2.25) = 0.0244$.

19. $z = (94.5 - 115)/12 = -1.71$. $P(X < 94.5) = P(Z < -1.71) = 0.0436$.
   Therefore, $(0.0436)(600) = 26$ students will be rejected.

21. $A = 7$, $B = 10$

   (a) $P[X \leq 8.8] = \dfrac{8.8 - 7}{3} = 0.600$

   (b) $P[7.4 < X < 9.5] = \dfrac{9.5 - 7.4}{3} = 0.700$

   (c) $P[X \geq 8.5] = \dfrac{10 - 8.5}{3} = 0.500$

Section 6.5 Normal Approximation to the Binomial

1. (a) From Table A.1 with $n = 15$ and $p = 0.2$ we have

   $$P(1 \leq X \leq 4) = \sum_{x=0}^{4} b(x; 15, 0.2) - b(0; 15, 0.2) = 0.8358 - 0.0352 = 0.8006.$$

   (b) By the normal-curve approximation we first find $\mu = np = 3$ and then $\sigma^2 = npq = (15)(0.2)(0.8) = 2.4$. Then $\sigma = 1.549$. Now, $z_1 = (0.5 - 3)/1.549 = -1.61$,
   $z_2 = (4.5 - 3)/1.549 = 0.97$ and
   $$P(1 \leq X \leq 4) = P(-1.61 \leq Z \leq 0.97)$$
   $$= 0.8340 - 0.0537 = 0.7803.$$

3.   n = 100;

    (a) p = 0.01;

$$\sigma = \sqrt{(100)(0.01)(0.99)} = 0.995; \ z = \frac{0.5 - 1.}{0.995} = -0.503;$$

$$P[X \le 0] \approx P[Z \le -0.503] = 0.3085.$$

    (b) p = 0.05;

$$\sigma = \sqrt{(100)(0.05)(0.95)} = 2.1794; \ z = \frac{0.5 - 5.}{2.1794} = -2.06;$$

$$P[X \le 0] \approx P[Z \le -2.06] = 0.0197.$$

5. $\mu = np = (100)(0.9) = 90$, and $\sigma = \sqrt{npq} = \sqrt{(100)(0.9)(0.1)} = 3$.

    (a) $z_1 = (83.5 - 90)/3 = -2.17$, $z_2 = (95.5 - 90)/3 = 1.83$.
        $P(83.5 < X < 95.5) = P(-2.17 < Z < 1.83) = 0.9664 - 0.0150$
        $= 0.9514$

    (b) $z = (85.5 - 90)/3 = -1.50$; $P(X < 85.5) = P(Z < -1.50)$
        $= 0.0668$.

7. $\mu = np = (1000)(0.2) = 200$, and $\sigma = \sqrt{npq} = \sqrt{(1000)(0.2)(0.8)}$
    $= 12.649$.

    (a) $z_1 = (169.5 - 200)/12.649 = -2.41$, $z_2 = (185.5 - 200)/12.649 = -1.15$;
        $P(169.5 < X < 185.5) = P(-2.41 < Z < -1.15) = 0.1251 - 0.0080 = 0.1171$.

    (b) $z_1 = (209.5 - 200)/12.649 = 0.75$, $z_2 = (225.5 - 200)/12.649 = 2.02$;
        $P(209.5 < X < 225.5) = P(0.75 < Z < 2.02) = 0.9783 - 0.7734 = 0.2049$.

9. $\mu = np = (180)(1/6) = 30$, $\sigma = \sqrt{npq} = \sqrt{(180)(1/6)(5/6)} = 5$,
    $z = (35.5 - 30)/5 = 1.1$. $P(X > 35.5) = P(Z > 1.1)$
    $= 1 - 0.8643 = 0.1357$.

11. $\mu = np = (400)(1/10) = 40$, and $\sigma = \sqrt{npq} = \sqrt{(400)(1/10)(9/10)} = 6$.
    (a) $z = (31.5 - 40)/6 = -1.42$; $P(X < 31.5) = P(Z < -1.42) = 0.0778$.
    (b) $z = (49.5 - 40)/6 = -1.58$; $P(X > 49.5) = P(Z > 1.58) = 1 - 0.9429 = 0.0571$.
    (c) $z = (34.5 - 40)/6 = -0.92$, $z_2 = (46.5 - 40)/6 = 1.08$;
        $P(34.5 < X < 46.5) = P(-0.92 < Z < 1.08) = 0.8599 - 0.1788$
        $= 0.6811$.

13.   (a) p = 0.05; n = 100;

$$\sigma = \sqrt{(100)(0.05)(0.95)} = 2.1794; \ z = \frac{2.5 - 5}{2.1794} = -1.147;$$

$$P[X \ge 2] \approx P[Z \ge -1.147] = 0.8749$$

    (b) $z = \dfrac{10.5 - 5}{2.1794} = 2.524$; $P[X > 10] \approx P[Z > 2.52] = 0.0059$

15. (a) $P[X > 230] = P\left[Z > \dfrac{230 - 170}{30}\right] = 0.0228$

(b) $z = \dfrac{8 - 6.84 - 0.5}{\sqrt{(300)(0.0228)(0.9772)}} = 0.26$

$P[X \geq 8] \approx P[Z > 0.26] = 0.3974$

Section 6.10 Weibull Distribution

1. $P[1.8 < X < 2.4] = \displaystyle\int_{1.8}^{2.4} x e^{-x} dx = [-x e^{-x} - e^{-x}]\Big|_{1.8}^{2.4}$

$= 2.8 e^{-1.8} - 3.4 e^{-2.4} = 0.1545.$

3. Setting $\alpha = 1/2$ on the gamma distribution and integrating, we have

$$\frac{1}{\sqrt{\beta}\,\Gamma(1/2)} \int_0^\infty x^{-1/2} e^{-x/\beta} dx = 1.$$

Substitute $x = y^2/2$, $dx = y\,dy$, to give

$$\Gamma(1/2) = \frac{\sqrt{2}}{\sqrt{\beta}} \int_0^\infty e^{-y^2/2\beta} dy = 2\sqrt{\pi}\left(\frac{1}{\sqrt{2\pi}\sqrt{\beta}} \int_0^\infty e^{-y^2/2\beta} dy\right) = \sqrt{\pi},$$

since the quantity in parentheses represents one-half of the area under the normal curve $n(y; 0, \sqrt{\beta})$.

5. (a) $\mu = \alpha\beta = (2)(3) = 6$ million liters;
$\sigma^2 = \alpha\beta^2 = (2)(9) = 18.$

(b) Water consumption on any given day has a probability of at least 3/4 of falling in the interval $\mu \pm 2\sigma = 6 \pm 2\sqrt{18}$ or from -2.485 to 14.485. That is, from 0 to 14.485 million liters.

7. $P(X < 3) = \dfrac{1}{4} \displaystyle\int_0^3 e^{-x/4} dx = -e^{-x/4}\Big|_0^3 = 1 - e^{-3/4} = 0.5276.$

Let Y = number of days a person is served in less than 3 minutes. Then

$P(Y \geq 4) = \displaystyle\sum_{x=4}^{6} b(y; 6, 1 - e^{-3/4}) = \binom{6}{4}(0.5276)^4 (0.4724)^2$

$+ \binom{6}{5}(0.5276)^5 (0.4724) + \binom{6}{6}(0.5276)^6 = 0.3968.$

9. (a) $E(X) = \displaystyle\int_0^\infty x^2 e^{-x^2/2} dx = -x e^{-x^2/2}\Big|_0^\infty + \int_0^\infty e^{-x^2/2}\, dx$

$= 0 + \sqrt{2\pi} \cdot \dfrac{1}{\sqrt{2\pi}} \displaystyle\int_0^\infty e^{-x^2/2} dx = \sqrt{2\pi}\,/\,2$

$= \sqrt{\pi/2} = 1.2533.$

(b) $P(X > 2) = \int_2^\infty xe^{-x^2/2}dx = -e^{-x^2/2}\Big|_2^\infty = e^{-2} = 0.1353.$

11. $R(t) = ce^{-\int 1/\sqrt{t}\,dt} = ce^{-2\sqrt{t}}$. However, $R(0) = 1$ and hence $c = 1$. Now,

$$f(t) = Z(t)R(t) = e^{-2\sqrt{t}}/\sqrt{t}, \ t > 0.$$

and

$$P(T > 4) = \int_4^\infty e^{-2\sqrt{t}}/\sqrt{t}\,dt = -e^{-2\sqrt{t}}\Big|_4^\infty = e^{-4} = 0.0183.$$

13. $\alpha = 5; \ \beta = 10;$
(a) $\alpha\beta = 50.$
(b) $\sigma^2 = \alpha\beta^2 = 500;$
$\sigma = \sqrt{500};$

(c) $P[X > 30] = \dfrac{1}{\beta^\alpha\Gamma(\alpha)}\int_{30}^\infty x^{\alpha-1}e^{-x/\beta}dx;$

Using the incomplete gamma with $y = x/\beta$, then

$$1 - P[X \le 30] = 1 - P[Y \le 3] = 1 - \int_0^3 \frac{y^4 e^{-y}}{\Gamma(5)}dy = 1 - 0.185 = 0.815.$$

15. $\mu = 3$ seconds, $\mu = \beta, \ \sigma^2 = \beta^2;$

$$f(x) = \frac{1}{3}e^{-x/3}$$

(a) $P[X > 5] = \int_5^\infty \dfrac{1}{3}e^{-x/3} = \dfrac{1}{3}[-3e^{-x/3}]\Big|_5^\infty = e^{-5/3} = 0.1889.$

(b) $P[X > 10] = e^{-10/3} = 0.0357.$

17. $\mu = E[X] = e^{4+4/2} = e^6; \ \sigma^2 = e^{8+4}(e^4 - 1) = e^{12}(e^4 - 1).$

19. (a) $P[X > 1] = 1 - P[X \le 1] =$

$$1 - 10\int_0^1 e^{-10x}dx = e^{-10} = 0.000045;$$

(b) $\mu = \beta = 1/10 = 0.1.$

Chapter 7
Functions of Random Variables

Section 7.3 Moments and Moment-Generating Functions

1. From $y = 2x - 1$ we obtain $x = (y + 1)/2$, and then
    $g(y) = f[(y + 1)/2] = 1/3$, $y = 1, 3, 5$.

3. The inverse functions of $y_1 = x_1 + x_2$ and $y_2 = x_1 - x_2$ are $x_1 = (y_1 + y_2)/2$
    and $x_2 = (y_1 - y_2)/2$. Therefore

    $$g(y_1, y_2) = \left(\begin{array}{c} 2 \\ \dfrac{y_1 + y_2}{2}, \dfrac{y_1 - y_2}{2}, 2 - y_1 \end{array} \right) \left(\frac{1}{4} \right)^{(y_1+y_2)/2} \left(\frac{1}{3} \right)^{(y_1-y_2)/2} \left(\frac{5}{12} \right)^{2-y_1},$$

    where $y_1 = 0, 1, 2$; and $y_2 = -2, -1, 0, 1, 2$; $y_2 \le y_1$; $y_1 + y_2 = 0, 2, 4$.

5. The inverse function of $y = -2 \ln x$ is given by $x = e^{-y/2}$ from which we obtain
    $|J| = |-e^{-y/2}/2| = e^{-y/2}/2$. Now,

    $$g(y) = f(e^{-y/2}) |J| = e^{-y/2}/2, \quad y > 0$$

    which is a chi-square distribution with 2 degrees of freedom.

7. To find k we solve the equation $k \int_0^\infty v^2 e^{-bv^2} dv = 1$. Let $x = bv^2$, $dx = 2bv\, dv$ and then
    $dv = (1/2\sqrt{b})x^{-1/2} dx$. Then our equation becomes

    $$\frac{k}{2b^{3/2}} \int_0^\infty x^{(3/2)-1} e^{-x} dx = 1, \text{ or } \frac{k\Gamma(3/2)}{2b^{3/2}} = 1.$$

    Hence $k = \dfrac{4b^{3/2}}{\Gamma(1/2)}$.

    Now the inverse function of $w = mv^2/2$ is $v = \sqrt{2w/m}$, $w > 0$, from which we obtain
    $|J| = 1/\sqrt{2mw}$. It follows that

    $$g(w) = f\left(\sqrt{2w/m}\right)|J| = \frac{4b^{3/2}}{\Gamma(1/2)}(2w/m)e^{-2bw/m}\frac{1}{\sqrt{2mw}}$$

    $$= \frac{1}{(m/2b)^{3/2}\Gamma(3/2)} w^{(3/2)-1} e^{-(2b/m)w}, \quad w > 0,$$

    which is a gamma distribution with $\alpha = 3/2$ and $\beta = m/2b$.

9.   (a)   The inverse of $y = x + 4$ is $x = y - 4$, $y > 4$, from which we obtain $|J| = 1$. Therefore, $g(y) = f(y-4)|J| = 32/y^3$, $y > 4$.

         (b) $P(Y > 8) = 32 \int_8^\infty y^{-3} dy = -16y^{-2}\big|_8^\infty = 1/4$.

11.   Amount of kerosene left at the end of the day is $Z = Y - X$.
Let $W = Y$. The inverse functions of $z = y - x$ and $w = y$ are $x = w - z$ and $y = w$,
$0 < z < w$, $0 < w < 1$, from which we obtain

$$J = \begin{vmatrix} \dfrac{\partial x}{\partial w} & \dfrac{\partial x}{\partial z} \\[2mm] \dfrac{\partial y}{\partial w} & \dfrac{\partial y}{\partial z} \end{vmatrix} = \begin{vmatrix} 1 & -1 \\ 1 & 0 \end{vmatrix} = 1.$$

Now, $g(w, z) = g(w - z, w) = 2$, $0 < z < w$, $0 < w < 1$
and the marginal distribution of Z is

$$h(z) = 2 \int_z^1 dw = 2(1 - z), \; 0 < z < 1.$$

13.   Since I and R are independent, the joint probability distribution is

$$f(i, r) = 12ri(1 - i), \; 0 < i < 1, \; 0 < r < 1.$$

Let $V = R$. The inverse functions of $w = i^2 r$ and $v = r$ are
$i = \sqrt{w/v}$ and $r = v$, $w < v < 1$, $0 < w < 1$, from which we obtain

$$J = \begin{vmatrix} \partial i/\partial w & \partial i/\partial v \\ \partial r/\partial w & \partial r/\partial v \end{vmatrix} = \frac{1}{2\sqrt{vw}}.$$

Then,

$$g(w, v) = f(\sqrt{w/v}, v), |J| = 12v\sqrt{w/v}(1 - \sqrt{w/v})\frac{1}{2\sqrt{vw}}$$
$$= 6(1 - \sqrt{w/v}), \; w < v < 1, \; 0 < w < 1.$$

and the marginal distribution of W is

$$h(w) = 6 \int_w^1 \left(1 - \sqrt{w/v}\right) dv = 6\left(v - 2\sqrt{w}\sqrt{v}\right)\Big|_{v=w}^{v=1}$$
$$= 6 + 6w - 12w^{1/2}, \; 0 < w < 1.$$

15. The inverse functions of $y = x^2$ are $x_1 = \sqrt{y}$, $x_2 = -\sqrt{y}$ for $0 < y < 1$ and $x_3 = \sqrt{y}$ for $1 < y < 4$. Now $|J_1| = |J_2| = |J_3| = 1/2\sqrt{y}$ from which we get

$$g(y) = f(\sqrt{y})|J_1| + f(-\sqrt{y})|J_2| = \frac{2(\sqrt{y}+1)}{9} \cdot \frac{1}{2\sqrt{y}} +$$

$$\frac{2(\sqrt{y}+1)}{9} \cdot \frac{1}{2\sqrt{y}} = 2/9\sqrt{y}, \quad 0 < y < 1$$

and

$$g(y) = f(\sqrt{y})|J_3| = \frac{2(\sqrt{y}+1)}{9} \cdot \frac{1}{2\sqrt{y}}$$

$$= (\sqrt{y}+1)/9\sqrt{y}, \quad 1 < y < 4.$$

17. $$M_X(t) = E(e^{tX}) = \frac{1}{k}\sum_{x=1}^{k} e^{tx} = \frac{1}{k}(e^t + e^{2t} + \cdots + e^{kt})$$

$$= \frac{e^t(1-e^{kt})}{k(1-e^t)}, \text{ by summing the geometric series of } k \text{ terms.}$$

19. $$M_X(t) = E(e^{tX}) = \sum_{x=0}^{\infty} \frac{e^{tx}e^{-\mu}\mu^x}{x!} = e^{-\mu}\sum_{x=0}^{\infty} \frac{(\mu e^t)^x}{x!}$$

$$= e^{-\mu}\left[1 + \frac{\mu e^t}{1!} + \frac{(\mu e^t)^2}{2!} + \cdots + \frac{(\mu e^t)^n}{n!} + \cdots\right]$$

$$= e^{-\mu}e^{\mu e^t} = e^{\mu(e^t-1)}.$$

Now,

$$\mu = M'_X(0) = \mu e^{\mu(e^t-1)+t}\Big|_{t=0} = \mu.$$

$$\mu'_2 = M''_X(0) = \mu e^{\mu(e^t-1)+t}(\mu e^t + 1)\Big|_{t=0} = \mu(\mu+1),$$

and

$$\sigma^2 = \mu'_2 - \mu^2 = \mu(\mu+1) - \mu^2 = \mu.$$

21. $$\mu = M'_X(0) = \nu(1-2t)^{\frac{-\nu}{2}-1}\Big|_{t=0} = \nu,$$

$$\mu'_2 = M''_X(0) = \nu(\nu+2)(1-2t)^{\frac{-\nu}{2}-2}\Big|_{t=0} = \nu(\nu+2),$$

and

$$\sigma^2 + \mu'_2 - \mu^2 = \nu(\nu+2) - \nu^2 = 2\nu.$$

Chapter 8
Fundamental Sampling Distributions
and Data Descriptions

Section 8.2 Some Important Statistics

1.   (a)   Responses of all people in Richmond who have telephones.
   (b)   Outcomes for a large or infinite number of tosses of a coin.
   (c)   Length of life of such tennis shoes when worn on the professional tour.
   (d)   All possible time intervals for this lawyer to drive from her home to her office.

3.   (a) $\bar{x} = 2.4$.   (b) $\tilde{x} = 2$.   (c) $m = 3$.

5.   (a) $\bar{x} = 3.2$ seconds.   (b) $\tilde{x} = 3.1$ seconds.

7.   (a) $\bar{x} = 53.75$.   (b)   Modes are 75 and 100.

9.   (a) Range $= 15 - 5 = 10$.

   (b) $s^2 = \dfrac{n\sum x^2 - \left(\sum x\right)^2}{n(n-1)} = \dfrac{(10)(838) - 86^2}{(10)(9)} = 10.933$.

   Taking the square root, we have $s = 3.307$.

11.   (a) $s^2 = \sum (x - \bar{x})^2 /(n-1) = [(2 - 2.4)^2 + (1 - 2.4)^2 + \cdots + (2 - 2.4)^2]/14$
    $= 2.971$.

   (b) $s^2 = \dfrac{n\sum x^2 - \left(\sum x\right)^2}{n(n-1)} = \dfrac{(15)(128) - 36^2}{(15)(14)} = 2.971$.

13. $s^2 = \dfrac{n\sum x^2 - \left(\sum x\right)^2}{n(n-1)} = \dfrac{(20)(148.55) - (53.3)^2}{(20)(19)} = 0.342$ and hence
    $s = 0.585$.

15. $s^2 = \dfrac{n\sum x^2 - \left(\sum x\right)^2}{n(n-1)} = \dfrac{(6)(207) - 33^2}{(6)(5)} = 5.1$.
    (a) Multiplying each observation by 3 gives $s^2 = (9)(5.1) = 45.9$.
    (b) Adding 5 to each value does not change the variance.
    Hence $s^2 = 5.1$.

Section 8.5 Sampling Distributions of Means

1. $z_1 = -1.9$, $z = -0.4$; $P(\mu_{\bar{x}} - 1.9\sigma_{\bar{x}} < \bar{X} < \mu_{\bar{x}} - 0.4\sigma_{\bar{x}})$
   $= P(-1.9 < Z < -0.4) = 0.3446 - 0.0287 = 0.3159$.

3. (a) For n = 64, $\sigma_{\bar{X}}$ = 5.6/8 = 0.7, whereas for n = 196,

$\sigma_{\bar{X}}$ = 5.6/14 = 0.4. Therefore, the standard error of the mean is reduced from 0.7 to 0.4 when the sample size is increased from 64 to 196.

(b) For n = 784, $\sigma_{\bar{X}}$ = 5.6/28 = 0.2, whereas for n = 49,

$\sigma_{\bar{X}}$ = 5.6/7 = 0.8. Therefore, the standard error of the mean is increased from 0.2 to 0.8 when the sample size is decreased from 784 to 49.

5. $\mu_{\bar{X}}$ = 240, $\sigma_{\bar{X}}$ = $15/\sqrt{40}$ = 2.372. Therefore $\mu_{\bar{X}} \pm 2\sigma_{\bar{X}}$ = 240 ± (2)(2.372) or from 235.257 to 244.743, which indicates that a value of x = 236 milliliters is reasonable and hence the machine need not be adjusted.

7. (a) $\mu = \sum xf(x) = (4)(0.2) + (5)(0.4) + (6)(0.3) + (7)(0.1) = 5.3,$

$\sigma^2 = \sum(x - \mu)^2 f(x) = (4 - 5.3)^2(0.2) + (5 - 5.3)^2(0.4)$
$\quad + (6 - 5.3)^2(0.3) + (7 - 5.3)^2(0.1) = 0.81.$

(b) With n = 36, $\mu_{\bar{X}} = \mu = 5.3$ and $\sigma_{\bar{X}}^2 = \sigma^2/n = 0.81/36 = 0.0225.$

(c) n = 36, $\mu_{\bar{X}} = 5.3$, $\sigma_{\bar{X}} = 0.9/6 = 0.15;$

z = (5.5 − 5.3)/0.15 = 1.33; $P(\bar{X} < 5.5) = P(Z < 1.33) = 0.9082.$

9. (a) $P[6.4 < \bar{x}\ 7.2] = P[-1.8 < Z < 0.6] = 0.6898;$
   (b) Using z = 1.04

$\bar{x} = z(\sigma/\sqrt{n}) + \mu = (1.04)(1/3) + 7 = 7.35;$

11. (a) $M_{\frac{\bar{X}-\mu}{\sigma/\sqrt{n}}}(t) = e^{\frac{-\mu\sqrt{n}t}{\sigma}} M_{\frac{\sqrt{n}\bar{X}}{\sigma}}(t)$ (Theorem 7.8)

$= e^{\frac{-\mu\sqrt{n}t}{\sigma}} M_{\sum X_i}\left(\frac{t}{\sigma/\sqrt{n}}\right)$ (Theorem 7.9)

$= e^{\frac{-\mu\sqrt{n}t}{\sigma}} \left[M_X\left(\frac{t}{\sigma/\sqrt{n}}\right)\right]^n.$ (Theorem 7.10)

Then,

$\ln M_{\frac{\bar{X}-\mu}{\sigma/\sqrt{n}}}(t) = -\frac{\mu\sqrt{n}t}{\sigma} + n\ln M_X\left(\frac{t}{\sigma/\sqrt{n}}\right).$

(b) From Exercise 22 of Section 7.3 we have

$M_X\left(\frac{t}{\sigma\sqrt{n}}\right) = 1 + \frac{\mu t}{\sigma\sqrt{n}} + \frac{\mu_2' t^2}{2!\sigma^2 n} + \frac{\mu_3' t^3}{3!\sigma^3 n\sqrt{n}} + \cdots = 1 + v.$

(c)   Using the Maclaurin series

$$\ln(1 + v) = v - \frac{v^2}{2} + \frac{v^3}{3} - \cdots, \; |v| < 1.$$

we obtain

$$M_{\frac{\overline{X}-\mu}{\sigma/\sqrt{n}}}(t) = \frac{-\mu\sqrt{n}t}{\sigma} + n = \left\{ \left[\frac{\mu t}{\sigma/\sqrt{n}} + \frac{\mu_2' t^2}{2!\sigma^2 n} + \frac{\mu_3' t^3}{3!\sigma^3 n\sqrt{n}} + \cdots \right] \right.$$

$$- \frac{1}{2}\left[\frac{\mu t}{\sigma/\sqrt{n}} + \frac{\mu_2' t^2}{2!\sigma^2 n} + \frac{\mu_3' t^3}{3!\sigma^3 n\sqrt{n}} + \cdots \right]^2$$

$$+ \frac{1}{3}\left[\frac{\mu t}{\sigma/\sqrt{n}} + \frac{\mu_2' t^2}{2!\sigma^2 n} + \frac{\mu_3' t^3}{3!\sigma^3 n\sqrt{n}} + \cdots \right]^3$$

$$\left. - \cdots \right\}$$

$$= \left(\frac{-\mu\sqrt{n}}{\sigma} + \frac{\mu\sqrt{n}}{\sigma} \right)t + \left(\frac{\mu_2'}{2\sigma^2} - \frac{(\mu_1')^2}{2\sigma^2} \right)t^2 + \text{terms which approach zero as } n \to \infty).$$

Therefore

$$\lim_{n\to\infty} \ln M_{\frac{\overline{X}-\mu}{\sigma/\sqrt{n}}}(t) = t^2/2$$

and hence

$$\lim_{n\to\infty} M_{\frac{\overline{X}-\mu}{\sigma/\sqrt{n}}}(t) = e^{t^2/2}.$$

13. $\mu_{\overline{X}_1-\overline{X}_2} = 72 - 28 = 44, \; \sigma_{\overline{X}_1-\overline{X}_2} = \sqrt{100/64 + 25/100} = 1.346;$

$z = (44.2 - 44)/1.346 = 0.15; \; P(\overline{X}_1 - \overline{X}_2 < 44.2) = P(Z < 0.15)$
$= 0.5596.$

15.   16.

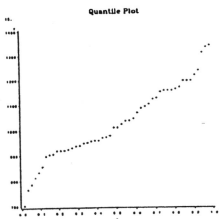

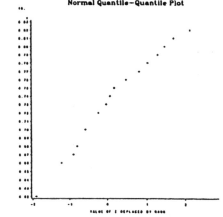

Section 8.8 F - Distribution

1. (a) 27.488; (b) 18.475; (c) 36.415.

3. (a) $\chi_\alpha^2 = \chi_{0.99}^2 = 0.297$; (b) $\chi_\alpha^2 = \chi_{0.025}^2 = 32.852$;

   (c) $\chi_{0.05}^2 = 37.652$. Therefore, $\alpha = 0.05 - 0.045 = 0.005$;

   Hence, $\chi_\alpha^2 = \chi_{0.005}^2 = 46.928$.

5. (a) $P(S^2 > 9.1) = P[(n - 1)S^2/\sigma^2 > (24)(9.1)/6] = P[\chi^2 > 36.4] = 0.05$;

   (b) $P[3.462 < S^2 < 10.745] = P[(24)(3.462)/6 < (n - 1)S^2/\sigma^2 < (24)(10.745)/6]$
   $P[13.848 < \chi^2 < 42.980] = 0.95 - 0.01 = 0.94$.

7. Since $(n - 1)S^2/\sigma^2$ is a chi-square statistic, it follows that

   $$\sigma^2_{(n-1)S^2/\sigma^2} = \frac{(n-1)^2}{\sigma^4}\sigma_{S^2}^2 = 2(n - 1).$$

   Hence, $\sigma_{S^2}^2 = \dfrac{2\sigma^4}{n-1}$, which decreases as n increases.

9. (a) $P(T < 2.365) = 1 - 0.025 = 0.975$.

   (b) $P(T > 1.318) = 0.10$.

   (c) $P(T < 2.179) = 1 - 0.025 = 0.975$; $P(T < -1.356) =$
   $P(T > 1.356) = 0.10$. Therefore, $P(-1.356 < T < 2.179) =$
   $0.975 - 0.10 = 0.875$.

   (d) $P(T > -2.567) = 1 - P(T > 2.567) = 1 - 0.01 = 0.99$.

11. (a) From Table A.4 we note that 2.069 corresponds to $t_{0.025}$ when $v = 23$. Therefore, $-t_{0.025}$ $= -2.069$ which means that the total area under the curve to the left of $t = k$ is $0.025 + 0.965 = 0.990$. Hence $k = t_{0.01} = 2.500$.

    (b) From Table A.4 we note that 2.807 corresponds to $t_{0.005}$ when $v = 23$. Therefore the total area under the curve to the right of $t = k$ is $0.095 + 0.005 = 0.10$. Hence $k = t_{0.10} = 1.319$.

    (c) Clearly $k = t_{0.05} = 1.714$ when $v = 23$ degrees of freedom.

13. $t = (24 - 20)/(4.1/3) = 2.927$; $t_{0.01} = 2.896$ with 8 degrees of freedom.
    Conclusion: No, $\mu > 20$.

15. (a) 2.71. (b) 3.51. (c) 2.92. (d) $1/2.11 = 0.47$.

    (e) $1/2.90 = 0.34$.

17. For H_0: Variances are equal, $F' = 1.44$

DF = (4, 5)   Prob > F' = 0.6872

The variances can be considered equal.

Chapter 9
One- and Two-Sample Estimation Problems

Section 9.7 Tolerance Limits

1.   From Example 9.1 we know that $E(S^2) = \sigma^2$. Therefore

$$E(S'^2) = E\left[\frac{n-1}{n}S^2\right] = \frac{n-1}{n}E[S^2] = \frac{n-1}{n}\sigma^2$$

3. $\lim\limits_{n\to\infty}\dfrac{np+\sqrt{n}/2}{n+\sqrt{n}} = \lim\limits_{n\to\infty}\dfrac{p+1/2\sqrt{n}}{1+1/\sqrt{n}} = p.$

5. $\sigma = 0.0015$, $n = 75$, $\bar{x}$ 0.310, $z = 1.96$.

$0.310 - (1.96)(0.0015/\sqrt{75}) < \mu < 0.310 + (1.96)(0.0015/\sqrt{75})$
$$0.3097 < \mu < 0.3103$$

7. $n = 100$, $\bar{x} = 23,500$, $\sigma = 3900$, $z_{0.005} = 2.575$.
       (a) $23,500 - (2.575)(3900/10) < \mu < 23,500 + (2.575)(3900/10)$
$$22,496 < \mu < 24,504.$$
       (b) $e < (2.575)(3900)/10 = 1004.$

9. $n = [(1.96)(0.0015)/(0.0005)]^2 = 35$ when rounded up

11. $n = [(2.575)(5.8)/2]^2 = 56$ when rounded up.

13. $n = 9$, $\bar{x} = 1.0056$, $s = 0.0245$, $t_{0.005} = 3.355$ with 8 degrees of freedom.

$1.0056 - (3.355)(0.0245/3) < \mu < 1.0056 + (3.355)(0.0245/3)$
$$0.978 < \mu < 1.033.$$

15. $n = 12$, $\bar{x} = 48.50$, $s = 1.5$, $t_{0.05} = 1.796$ with 11 degrees of freedom.
$48.50 - (1.796)(1.5/3.464) < \mu < 48.50 + (1.796)(1.5/3.464)$
$$47.722 < \mu < 49.278.$$

17. $s = 0.5$, $\bar{x} = 325.05$, $\gamma = 5\%$, $1 - \alpha = 90\%$, $k = 2.208$.
$325.05 \pm (2.208)(0.5)$
$[323.95, 326.15]$

19. $n = 100$, $\bar{x} = 23,500$, $s = 3900$, $1 - \alpha = 0.99$, $\gamma = 0.01$,
       $k = 3.096$. Tolerance interval is
$$\bar{x} \pm ks = 23,500 \pm (3,096)(3900)$$
       or 11,426 to 35,574.

Section 9.9 Paired Observations

1. $n_1 = 25$, $n_2 = 36$, $\bar{x}_1 = 80$, $\bar{x}_2 = 75$, $\sigma_1 = 5$, $\sigma_2 = 3$, $z_{0.03} = 1.88$.

$$(80 - 75) - 1.88\sqrt{25/25 + 9/36} < \mu_1 - \mu_2 < (80 - 75) + 1.88\sqrt{25/25 + 9/36}$$
$$2.9 < \mu_1 - \mu_2 < 7.1$$

3. $n_1 = 100$, $n_2 = 200$, $x_1 = 12.2$, $x_2 = 9.1$, $s_1 = 1.1$, and $s_2 = 0.9$, $z_{0.01} = 2.327$.

$$(12.2 - 9.1) - 2.33\sqrt{(1.1^2/100) + (0.9^2/200)} < \mu_1 - \mu_2$$
$$< (12.2 - 9.1) + 2.33\sqrt{(1.1^2/100) + (0.9^2/200)}$$

Simplifying, we obtain
$$2.80 < \mu_1 - \mu_2 < 3.40.$$
The treatment appears to reduce the mean amount of metal removed.

5. $n_1 = 12$, $n_2 = 18$, $\bar{x}_1 = 84$, $\bar{x} = 77$, $s_1 = 4$, $s_2 = 6$, $s_p = 5.305$, $t_{0.005} = 2.763$ with 28 degrees of freedom.

$$(84 - 77) = (2.763)(5.305)\sqrt{1/12 + 1/18} < \mu_1 - \mu_2 < (84 - 77)$$
$$+ (2.763)(5.305)\sqrt{1/12 + 1/18}$$

Simplifying, we get
$$1.5 < \mu_1 - \mu_2 < 12.5.$$

7. $n_1 = 14$, $n_2 = 16$, $x_1 = 17$, $x_2 = 19$, $s_1 = 1.5$, $s_2 = 1.8$
$s_p = 1.289$, $t_{0.005} = 2.763$ with 28 degrees of freedom.

$$(19 - 17) \pm (2.763)(1.289)\sqrt{\frac{1}{16} + \frac{1}{14}} \text{ gives}$$

(2 ± 1.30)
Simplifying, we get: $(0.70 < \mu_2 - \mu_1 < 3.30$.

9. $n_1 = 12$, $n_2 = 12$, $\bar{x}_1 = 36{,}300$, $\bar{x}_2 = 38{,}100$, $s1 = 5000$, $s_2 = 6100$,

$$v = \frac{\left((5000)^2/12 + (6100)^2/12\right)}{\left[\dfrac{\left((5000)^2/12\right)^2}{11} + \dfrac{\left((6100)^2/12\right)^2}{11}\right]} = 21.$$

So $t_{0.025} = 2.080$ with 21 degrees of freedom.

$$(36{,}300 - 38{,}100) \pm (2.080)\sqrt{\frac{5000^2}{12} + \frac{6100^2}{12}}$$

(-1800 ± 4735.9)
Simplifying, we get $-6536 < \mu_1 - \mu_2 < 2936$.

11. $n = 9$, $\bar{d} = 2.778$, $s_d = 4.5765$, $t_{0.025} = 2.306$ with 8 degrees of freedom.

$$2.778 - (2.306)(4.5765)/3 < \mu_D < 2.778 + (2.306)(4.5765)/3 - .74 < \mu_D < 6.30.$$

13. $s_d = 30.4868$, $n = 10$, $\bar{d} = 14.89\%$, $t_9 = 2.262$;

$14.89 - (2.262)(30.4868)/\sqrt{10} < \mu_d < 14.89 + (2.262)(30.4868)/\sqrt{10}$

$-6.92 < \mu_d < 36.70$

Section 9.11 Two Samples: Estimating the Difference Between Two Proportions

1. (a) $n = 200$, $\hat{p} = 0.57$, $\hat{q} = 0.43$, $z_{0.02} = 2.05$.

$0.57 - 2.05\sqrt{(0.57)(0.43)/200} < p < 0.57 + 2.05\sqrt{(0.57)(0.43)/200}$

$0.498 < p < 0.642$

(b) Error $\leq 2.05\sqrt{(0.57)(0.43)/200} = 0.072$

3. $n = 1000$ $\hat{p} = 0.228$, $z_{0.005} = 2.575$.

$.228 - 2.575\sqrt{(.228)(.772)/1000} < p < .228 + 2.575\sqrt{(.228)(.772)/1000}$

$$0.194 < p < 0.262.$$

5. (a) $n = 40$, $\hat{p} = 34/40 = 0.85$, $z_{0.025} = 1.96$.

$0.85 - 1.96\sqrt{(0.85)(0.15)/40} < p < 0.85 + 1.96\sqrt{(0.85)(0.15)/40}$

$$0.739 < p < 0.961.$$

(b) Since p = 0.8 falls in the confidence interval, we can not conclude that the new system is better.

7. $n = 1600$, $\hat{p} = 2/3$, $z_{0.025} = 1.96$.

(a) $2/3 - 1.96\sqrt{(2.3)(1/3)/1600} < p < 2/3 + 1.96\sqrt{(2/3)(1/3)/1600}$

Error $\leq 1.96\sqrt{(2/3)(1/3)/1600} = 0.023$.

9. $n = (2.05)^2(0.57)(0.43)/(0.02)^2 = 2576$ when rounded up.

11. $n = (2.33)^2(0.08)(0.92)/(0.05)^2 = 160$ when rounded up.

13. $n = (2.575)^2/(4)(0.01)^2 = 16,577$ when rounded up.

15. $n_1 = n_2 = 1000$, $\hat{p}_M = 0.250$, $\hat{q}_M = 0.750$, $\hat{p}_F = 0.275$, $\hat{q}_F = 0.725$, $z_{0.025} = 1.96$.

$(0.275 - 0.250) - 1.96\sqrt{(0.250)(0.750)/1000 + (0.275)(0.725)/1000}$

$< p_F - p_M < (0.275 - 0.250)$

$\qquad + 1.96\sqrt{(0.250)(0.750)/1000 + (0.275)(0.725)/1000}$

Hence,

$\qquad -0.0136 < p_F - p_M < 0.0636.$

17. $n_1 = n_2 = 500$, $\hat{p}_1 = 0.24$, $\hat{q}_1 = 0.76$, $\hat{p}_2 = 0.196$, $\hat{q}_2 = 0.804$, $z_{0.05} - 1.645$.

$(0.24 - 0.196) - 1.645\sqrt{(0.24)(0.76)/500 + (0.196)(0.804)/500}$
$< p_1 - p_2 < (0.24 - 0.196)$
$\qquad + 1.645\sqrt{(0.24)(0.76)/500 + (0.196)(0.804)/500}$

Hence,
$\qquad 0.0011 < p_1 - p_2 < 0.0869.$ $\qquad$ Valid claim.

19. $n = 1000$, $n_{1991} = 760$, $\hat{p} = 0.2740$, $\hat{p}_{1991} = 0.3158$.

$(0.2740 - 0.3158) \pm (1.96)\sqrt{(0.2740)(0.7260)/1000 + (0.3158)(0.6842)/760}$
$-0.0849 < p - p_{1991} < 0.0013$

Since the interval includes ∅, significance cannot be shown.

Section 9.13 Two Samples: Estimating the Ratio of Two Variances

1. $s^2 = 0.815$, $\nu = 4$ degrees of freedom, $\chi^2_{0.025} = 11.143$, $\chi^2_{0.975} = 0.484$.

$\qquad (4)(0.815)/11.143 < \sigma^2 < (4)(0.815)/0.484$
$\qquad\qquad 0.293 < \sigma^2 < 6.736.$

Since this interval contains the value 1, the claim that $\sigma^2 = 1$ is valid.

3. $s^2 = 6.0025$, $\nu = 19$ degrees of freedom, $\chi^2_{0.025} = 32.852$, $\chi^2_{0.975} = 8.907$.

$\qquad (19)(6.0025)/32.852 < \sigma^2 < (19)(6.0025)/8.907$
$\qquad\qquad 3.472 < \sigma^2 < 12.804$
$\qquad\qquad 1.863 < \sigma < 3.578.$

5. $s^2 = 225$, $\nu = 9$ degrees of freedom, $\chi^2_{0.005} = 23.589$, $\chi^2_{0.995} = 1.735$

$(9)(225)/23.589 < \sigma^2 < (9)(225)/1.735$
$85.84 < \sigma^2 < 1167.15$
$9.265 < \sigma < 34.164.$

7. $s_1^2 = 1.00$, $s_2^2 = 0.64$, $f_{0.01}(11, 9) = 5.19$, $f_{0.01}(9, 11) = 4.63$.

$\qquad (1.00/0.64)(1/5.19) < \sigma_1^2 / \sigma_2^2 < (1.00/0.64)(4.63)$
$\qquad\qquad 0.301 < \sigma_1^2 / \sigma_2^2 < 7.234$
$\qquad\qquad 0.549 < \sigma_1 / \sigma_2 < 2.690.$

9. $s_I^2 = 76.3$, $s_{II}^2 = 1035.905$, $f_{0.05}(4, 6) = 4.53$, $f_{0.05}(6, 4) = 6.16$.

$\qquad (76.3/1035.905)(1/4.53) < \sigma_1^2 / \sigma_2^2 < (76.3/1035.905)(6.16)$
$\qquad\qquad 0.016 < \sigma_1^2 / \sigma_2^2 < 0.454.$

Therefore, $\sigma_1^2 \neq \sigma_2^2$.

Section 9.14 Bayesian Methods of Estimation

1. For $p = 0.1$, $b(2; 2, 0.1) = \binom{2}{2}(0.1)^2 = 0.01$.

   For $p = 0.2$, $b(2; 2, 0.2) = \binom{2}{2}(0.2)^2 = 0.04$.

   A: number of defectives in our sample is 2,
   B_1: proportion of defectives is $p = 0.1$,
   B_2: proportion of defectives is $p = 0.2$.

   $$P(B_1 \mid A) = \frac{(0.6)(0.01)}{(0.6)(0.01) + (0.4)(0.04)} = 0.27$$

   and then by substitution $P(B_2 \mid A) = 1 - 0.27 = 0.73$. Hence the posterior distribution is

p	0.1	0.2
$f(p \mid x = 2)$	0.27	0.73

   for which we get
   $p^* = (0.1)(0.27) + (0.2)(0.73) = 0.173$.

3. (a) Let $X =$ the number of drinks that overflow. Then

   $$f(x \mid p) = b(x; 4, p) = \binom{4}{x} p^x q^{4-x}, \quad x = 0, 1, 2, 3, 4.$$

   Now,

   $$f(1, p) = f(1 \mid p)f(p) = 10\binom{4}{1}pq^3 = 40p(1 - p)^3,$$
   $$0.05 < p < 0.15.$$

   Therefore,

   $$g(1) = 40 \int_{0.05}^{0.15} p(1-p)^3 dp = -2(1-p)^4(4p+1)\Big|_{0.05}^{0.15}$$
   $$= 0.2844,$$
   and then
   $$f(p \mid x = 1) = 40p(1 - p)^3/0.2844.$$

   (b) $p^* = \dfrac{40}{0.2844} \int_{0.05}^{0.15} p^2(1-p)^3 dp$

   $$= \frac{40}{(0.2844)(60)} p^3(20 - 45p + 36p^2 - 10p^3)\Big|_{0.05}^{0.15}$$
   $$= 0.106.$$

5. $\sigma = 0.8$, $\mu_0 = 8$, $\sigma_0 = 0.2$, $n = 10$, $\bar{x} = 9$, $z_{0.025} = 1.96$.

$$\mu_1 = \frac{(10)(9)(0.04) + (8)(0.64)}{(10)(0.04) + 0.64} = 8.3846.$$

$$\sigma_1 = \sqrt{\frac{(0.04)(0.64)}{(10)(0.04) + 0.64}} = 0.1569.$$

$$8.3846 - (1.96)(0.1569) < \mu < 8.3846 + (1.96)(0.1569)$$
$$8.077 < \mu < 8.692.$$

7.   (a) $z_1 = (71.8 - 72)/2.4 = -0.08$, $z_2 = (73.4 - 72)/2.4 - 0.58$;
            $P(71.8 < X < 73.4) = P(-0.08 < Z < 0.58) = 0.7190 - 0.4681$
            $= 0.2509$.

      (b) $\mu_0 = 72$, $\sigma_0^2 = 5.76$, $n = 100$, $\bar{x} = 70$, $s^2 = 64$.

$$\mu_1 = \frac{(100)(70)(5.76) + (72)(64)}{(100)(5.76) + 64} = 70.2,$$

$$\sigma_1 = \sqrt{\frac{(5.76)(64)}{(100)(5.76) + 64}} = 0.759.$$

$$70.2 - (1.96)(0.759) < \mu < 70.2 + (1.96)(0.759)$$
$$68.71 < \mu < 71.69.$$

      (c) $z_1 = (71.8 - 70.2)/0.759 = 2.11$, $z_2 = (73.4 - 70.2)/0.759$
            $= 4.22$;
            $P(71.8 < X < 73.4) = P(2.11 < Z < 4.22) = 1 - 0.9826 = 0.0174$.

9.   Multiplying the density of our sample

$$f(t_1, t_2, \ldots, t_n \mid \theta) = \theta^n e^{-\theta \sum_{i=1}^{n} t_i}$$

by our prior

$$f(\theta) = 2e^{-2\theta}, \; \theta > 0,$$

we obtain

$$f(t_1, t_2, \ldots, t_n, \theta) = 2\theta^n e^{-\theta \left(\sum_{i=1}^{n} t_i + 2 \right)}.$$

Now,

$$g(t_1, t_2, \ldots, t_n) = 2 \int_0^{\infty} \theta^n e^{-\theta \left(\sum_{i=1}^{n} t_i + 2 \right)} d\theta.$$

Let $u = \theta\left(\sum_{i=1}^{n} t_i + 2\right)$, $du = \theta\left(\sum_{i=1}^{n} t_i + 2\right)d\theta$, and then

$$g(t_1, t_2, \ldots, t_n) = \frac{2}{\left(\sum_{i=1}^{n} t_i + 2\right)^{n+1}} \int_{0}^{\infty} u^{(n+1)-1} e^{-u} du$$

$$= \frac{2\Gamma(n+1)}{\left(\sum_{i=1}^{n} t_i + 2\right)^{n+1}}$$

$f(\theta \mid t_1, t_2, \ldots, t_n) = f(t_1, t_2, \ldots, t_n, \theta)/g(t_1, t_2, \ldots, t_n)$

$$= \frac{\left(\sum_{i=1}^{n} t_i + 2\right)^{n+1}}{\Gamma(n+1)} \theta^n e^{-\theta\left(\sum_{i=1}^{n} t_i + 2\right)}, \theta > 0,$$

which is a gamma distribution with $\alpha = n + 1$ and

$$\beta = 1/\left(\sum_{i=1}^{n} t_i + 2\right).$$

Section 9.15 Maximum Liklihood Estimation

1. $L(x_1, \ldots, x_n) = \prod_{i=1}^{n} f(x_i, p) = \prod_{i=1}^{n} p^{x_i}(1-p)^{(1-x_i)}$,

   $\ln L = \sum_{i=1}^{n} x_i \ln(p) + \sum_{i=1}^{n} (1-x_i)\ln(1-p)$,

   $\dfrac{\partial \ln L}{\partial} = \dfrac{\sum x_i}{p} - \dfrac{n - \sum x_i}{(1-p)} = 0$,

   $\dfrac{\sum x_i}{p} = \dfrac{n - \sum x_i}{(1-p)}$

   $\hat{p} = \dfrac{\sum x_i}{n}$.

3.   (a) $L(x_1, \ldots, x_n) = \prod_{i=1}^{n} f(x_i, \mu, \sigma) = \prod_{i=1}^{n}\left[\dfrac{1}{\sqrt{2\pi}\sigma x_i} e^{-[\ln(x_i)-\mu]^2/2\sigma^2}\right]$

     (b) $\ln L = \dfrac{-n}{2}\ln(2\pi) - \dfrac{n}{2}\ln(\sigma^2) - \sum \ln(x_i) - \dfrac{1}{2\sigma^2}\sum_i [\ln(x_i)-\mu]^2$

         $\dfrac{\partial \ln L}{\partial \mu} = +\dfrac{\sum \ln(x_i)}{\sigma^2} - \dfrac{n\mu}{\sigma^2} = 0$

         $\hat{\mu} = \dfrac{\sum \ln(x_i)}{n}$

5. $L(X) = p^x(1-p)^{1-x}$,
    $\ln L = x \ln(p) - (1-x) \ln(1-p)$,

    $$\frac{\partial \ln L}{\partial p} = \frac{x}{p} - \frac{(1-x)}{(1-p)} = 0,$$

    $(1-p)x - p(1-x) = 0$,
    $\hat{p} = x = 1$.

Chapter 10
One- and Two-Sample Tests of Hypotheses

Section 10.4 The Use of P-Values for Decision Making

1. (a) Conclude that fewer than 30% of the public are allergic to some cheese products when in fact 30% or more are allergic.

    (b) Conclude that at least 30% of the public are allergic to some cheese products when in fact fewer than 30% are allergic.

3. (a) The firm is not guilty.
    (b) The firm is guilty.

5. (a) $\alpha = [P[X < 110 \mid p = 0.6] + P[X > 130 \mid p = 0.6] = P[Z < -1.52] + P[Z > 1.52]$
        $= 2(0.0643) = 0.1286.$

    (b) $\beta = P[110 < X < 130 \mid p = 0.5] = P[1.34 < Z < 4.31] = 0.0901;$
        $\beta = P[110 < X < 130 \mid p = 0.7] = P[-4.71 < Z < -1.47] = 0.0708.$

    (c) The probability of a Type I error is somewhat high for this test procedure.

7. (a) $\alpha = P[X \le 24 \mid p = 0.6] = P[Z < -1.59] = 0.0559.$
    (b) $\beta = P[X > 24 \mid p = 0.3] = P[Z > 2.93] = 1. - 0.9983 = 0.0017;$
        $\beta = P[X > 24 \mid p = 0.4] = P[Z > 1.30] = 1. - 0.9032 = 0.0968;$
        $\beta = P[X > 24 \mid p = 0.5] = P[Z > -0.14] = 1. - 0.4443 = 0.5557.$

9. (a) $p = 0.7, \ n = 100, \ \mu = np = 70, \ \sigma = \sqrt{npq} = \sqrt{(100)(0.7)(0.3)}$
        $= 4.583, \ z = (82.5 - 70)/4.583 = 2.73.$
        Therefore,
        $$\alpha = P(X > 82) = P(Z > 2.73) = 1 - P(Z < 2.73)$$
        $$= 1 - 0.9968 = 0.0032.$$

    (b) $p = 0.9, \ n = 100, \ \mu = 90, \ \sigma = \sqrt{npq} = \sqrt{(100)(0.9)(0.1)} = 3,$
        $z = (82.5 - 90)/3 = -2.5.$
        Therefore, $\beta = P(X \le 82) = P(Z < -2.5) = 0.0062.$

11. (a) $n = 70, p = 0.4, \mu = np = 28, \sigma = \sqrt{npq} = \sqrt{(70)(0.4)(0.6)} = 4.099,$
        $z = (23.5 - 28)/4.099 = -1.10.$
        Therefore, $\alpha = P(X < 24) = P(Z < -1.10) = 0.1357.$

    (b) $n = 70, p = 0.3, \mu = 21, \sigma = \sqrt{npq} = \sqrt{(70)(0.3)(0.7)} = 3.834,$
        $z = (23.5 - 21)/3.834 = 0.65.$ Therefore,
        $\beta = 1 - P[X < 24] = 1 - P[Z < 0.65] = 1 - 0.7422 = 0.2578.$

13. From Exercise 12(a) we have $\mu = 240$ and $\sigma = 9.798$. Then $z_1 = (214.5 - 240)/9.798 = -2.60$, $z_2 = (265.5 - 240)/9.798 = 2.60$.

$$\alpha = P(X \leq 214) + P(X \geq 266) = P(Z < -2.60) + P(Z > 2.60)$$
$$= 2P(Z < -2.60) = (2)(0.0047) = 0.0094.$$

From Exercise 12(b) with $\mu = 192$ and $\sigma = 9.992$ we obtain $z_1 = (214.5 - 192)/9.992 = 2.25$, $z_2 = (265.6 - 192)/9.992 = 7.36$.

$$\beta = P(214 < X < 266) = P(2.25 < Z < 7.36)$$
$$= 1 - 0.9878 = 0.0122.$$

15. (a) $\mu = 200$, $n = 9$, $\sigma = 15$, $\sigma_{\bar{X}} = 15/3 = 5$.
$z_1 = (191 - 200)/5 = -1.8$, $z_2 = (209 - 200)/5 = 1.8$.
$\alpha = P(Z < -1.8) + P(Z > 1.8) = 2P(Z < -1.8)$
$= (2)(0.0359) = 0.0718$.

(b) If $\mu = 215$, $z_1 = (191 - 215)/5 = -4.8$ and $z_2 = (209 - 215)/5 = -1.2$. Then $\beta = P(-4.8 < Z < -1.2) = 0.1151 - 0 = 0.1151$.

17. (a) $\mu = 5000$, $n = 50$, $\alpha = 120$, $\sigma_{\bar{x}} = 120/\sqrt{50} = 16.971$.
$z = (4970 - 5000)/16.971 = -1.77$; $\alpha = P(Z < -1.77) = 0.0384$.

(b) If $\mu = 4970$, $z = 0$ and $\beta = P(Z > 0) = 0.5$.
If $\mu = 4960$, $z = (4970 - 4960/16.971 = 0.59$ and $\beta = P(Z > 0.59) = 0.2776$.

Section 10.10 Graphical Methods for Comparing Means

1. H_0: $\mu = 800$
H_1: $\mu \neq 800$

$$z = \frac{788 - 800}{40} = -1.64; \quad P\text{-value} = 0.10.$$

The mean is not significantly different from 800 for $\alpha < 0.10$.

3. H_0: $\mu = 40$ months
H_1: $\mu < 40$ months
$\alpha = 0.025$.
Critical region: $z < -1.96$.
Computations: $z = (38 - 40)/(5.8/\sqrt{64}) = -2.76$.
Decision: Reject H_0, $\mu < 40$ months. $P = 0.0029$.

5. H_0: $\mu = 20{,}000$
H_1: $\mu > 20{,}000$
$\alpha = 0.01$.
Critical region: $z > 2.33$.
Computations: $z = (23{,}500 - 20{,}000)/(3900/10) = 8.97$.
Decision: Reject H_0, $\mu > 20{,}000$ kilometers. $P < 0.0001$

7. H_0: $\mu = 10$.
    H_1: $\mu \neq 10$.
    $\alpha = 0.01$.

    Critical region: $t < -3.25$ and $t > 3.25$.
    Computations: $t = (10.06 - 10)/(0.246/\sqrt{10}) = 0.77$.
    Decision: Do not reject H_0.

9. $$s_p = \sqrt{\frac{29(10.5)^2\, 29(10.2)^2}{58}} = 10.35$$

    $$P\left[Z > \frac{34.0}{10.35\sqrt{\dfrac{1}{30} + \dfrac{1}{30}}}\right] = P[Z > 12.72] = 1 - (\sim 1) \cong 0.00$$

    The P-value would be very close to zero.
    The conclusion is that running increases the mean (RMR) in older women.

11. H_0: $\mu = 35$ min.
    H_1: $\mu < 35$ min.
    $$t = \frac{33.1 - 35.}{\dfrac{4.3}{\sqrt{20}}} = -1.98; \text{ P-value} = 0.0312.$$

    Reject H_0, it takes less than 35 minutes, on the average, to take the test.

13. H_0: $\mu_A - \mu_B = 12$
    H_1: $\mu_A - \mu_B < 12$
    $\alpha = 0.05$
    Critical region: $z < -1.645$
    $$z = \frac{(86.7 - 77.8 - 12)}{\sqrt{(6.28)^2/50 + (5.62)^2/50}} = -2.60$$

    Reject H_0, the average tensile strength of thread A is less than 12 kilograms higher than the average tensile strength of thread B.

15. H_0: $\mu_1 - \mu_2 = 0.5$ micromoles per 30 min.
    H_1: $\mu_1 - \mu_2 > 0.5$ micromoles per 30 min.
    $\alpha = 0.01$.
    Critical region: $t > 2.485$.
    Computations: $s_p^2 = [(14)(1.5)^2 + (11)(1.2)^2]/25 = 1.8936.$ $s_p = 1.376$

    $$t = (8.8 - 7.5 - 0.5)/1.376\sqrt{1/15 + 1/12} = 1.50$$
    Decision: Do not reject H_0.

17. H_1: $\mu_1 = \mu_2$
     H_1: $\mu_1 < \mu_2$
     $\alpha = 0.05$.
     Critical region: $t < -1.895$.
     Computations: $s_1^2 = 1.363$, $s_2^2 = 3.883$, $s_p^2 = [(3)(1.363) + (4)(3.883)]/7 = 2.803$,
     $\quad\quad\quad\quad\quad s_p = 1.674$.
     $\quad\quad\quad\quad\quad t = (2.075 - 2.860)/1.674\sqrt{1/4 + 1/5} = -0.70$.
     Decision: Do not reject H_0.

19. H_0: $\mu_1 - \mu_2 = 4$ kilometers.
     H_1: $\mu_1 - \mu_2 \neq 4$ kilometers.
     $\alpha = 0.10$.
     Critical region: $t < -1.725$ and $t > 1.725$.
     Computations: $t = (5 - 4)/(0.915)\sqrt{1/12 + 1/10} = 2.55$.
     Decision: Reject H_0, $\mu_1 - \mu_2 > 4$ kilometers.

21. H_0: $\mu_{II} - \mu_I = 10$
     H_1: $\mu_{II} - \mu_I > 10$
     $\alpha = 0.01$.
     Critical region: $s_I^2 = 78.800$, $s_{II}^2 = 913.333$,

     $$v = \frac{(78.8/5 + 913.333/7)^2}{(78.8/5)^2/4 + (913.333/7)^2/6} = 7 \text{ degrees of freedom.}$$

     Hence, $t' > 2.998$ is our critical region.
     Computations: $\bar{x}_I = 97.4$, $\bar{x}_{II} = 110$,
     $\quad\quad\quad\quad\quad t' = (110 - 97.4 - 10)/\sqrt{78.800/5 + 913.333/7} = 0.22$.
     Decision: Do not reject H_0:

23. H_0: $\mu_1 = \mu_2$
     H_1: $\mu_1 \neq \mu_2$
     $\alpha = 0.05$.
     Critical region: $s_1 = 7874.329$, $s_2 = 2479.503$,

     $$v = \frac{(7874.329^2/16 + 2479.503^2/12)}{(7874.329^2/16)^2/15 + (2479.503^2/12)^2/11} = 19 \text{ degrees of freedom.}$$

     Hence, our critical region is $t' < -2.093$ and $t' > 2.093$.
     Computations: $\bar{x}_1 = 9897.500$, $\bar{x}_2 = 4120.833$, and
     $\quad\quad\quad\quad\quad t' = (9897.500 - 4120.833)/\sqrt{7874.329^2/16 + 2479.503^2/12}$
     $\quad\quad\quad\quad\quad = 2.76$.
     Decision: Reject H_0, $\mu_1 > \mu_2$.

25. H_0: $\mu_1 = \mu_2$
H_1: $\mu_1 > \mu_2$
$\alpha = 0.025$.
Critical region: $t > 2.201$.
Computations: $s_d = 0.198$, $\bar{d} = 0.14$. Therefore

$$t = \frac{0.1417}{\frac{0.198}{\sqrt{12}}} = 2.48; \ \ \text{P-value} = 0.0303.$$

Reject H_0, radial tires give better fuel economy.

27. H_0: $\mu_1 = \mu_2$
H_1: $\mu_1 < \mu_2$
$\alpha = 0.05$.
Critical region: $t < 1.761$.
Computations: $\bar{d} = -54.13$, $s_d = 83.002$. Therefore

$$t = -54.13/(83.002/\sqrt{15}) = -2.53.$$

Decision: Reject H_0, valid claim.

29. $n = \dfrac{(1.645 + 1.282)^2 (0.24)^2}{(0.3)^2} = 5.48$

The sample size would be 6.

31. $1 - \beta = 0.95$, $\beta = 0.05$, $\alpha = 0.02$, $\delta = 3.1$, $z_{0.05} = 1.645$, $z_{0.01} = 2.33$. Hence

$$n = (2.33 + 1.645)^2 (6.9)^2/(3.1)^2 = 79.$$

33. $n = \dfrac{(1.645 + 0.842)^2 (2.25)^2}{[1.2(2.25)]^2} = 4.29$

The sample size would be 5.

35. (a) H_0: $M_{hot} - M_{cold} = 0$
   H_1: $M_{hot} - M_{cold} \neq 0$

   (b) Paired t. $t = 0.99$; do not reject. $P = 0.36$.

Section 10.12 Two Sample: Tests on Two Proportion

1. For H_0: $p = 0.40$
   H_1: $p > 0.40$ $X =$ Those who choose lasagne
   $P[X \geq 9 \mid p = 0.40] = 0.4044$ (The claim that $p = 0.40$ is not refuted.)

   For H_0: $p = 0.40$
   H_1: $p \neq 0.40$
   A candidate rejection region would be
   $P[X \leq 4 \mid p = 0.40] + P[X \geq 16 \mid p = 0.40] = 0.0513$.
   The claim that $p = 0.40$ when $X = 9$ is observed is again reasonable.

3. H_0: $p = 0.5$
   H_1: $p < 0.5$

   $$P = P[X \le 5 \mid p = 0.05] = \sum_{x=0}^{5} b(x; 20, 0.5) = 0.0207;$$

   Reject H_0, the coin is not balanced.

5. H_0: $p = 0.20$
   H_1: $p < 0.20$

   $$z = \frac{136 - 200}{\sqrt{1000(0.20)(0.80)}} = -5.06 \; P[Z < -5.06] \cong 0.$$

   Decision: Reject H_0, less than 1/5 of the homes in the city are heated by oil.

7. H_0: $p = 0.8$
   H_1: $p > 0.8$

   $$z = \frac{250 - 240}{\sqrt{(300)(0.8)(0.2)}} = 1.44,$$

   $P[X \ge 250] \cong P[Z > 1.44] = 0.0749;$
   At $\alpha = 0.04$ it cannot be concluded that the new missile system is more accurate.
   However, with a P-value = 0.06 more trials should be considered.

9. H_0: $p_1 = p_2$
   H_1: $p_1 \ne p_2$

   $$z = \frac{0.63 - 0.472}{\sqrt{(0.5422)(0.4578)\left[\dfrac{1}{100} + \dfrac{1}{125}\right]}} = 2.36$$

   $P[Z < -2.36] + P[Z > 2.36] = 0.0182;$
   The proportion of urban residents who favor the nuclear plant is larger than the proportion of suburban residents who favor the nuclear plant.

11. H_0: $p_U = p_R$
    H_1: $p_U > p_R$

    $$z = \frac{0.10 - 0.0667}{\sqrt{(0.0857)(0.9143)\left[\dfrac{1}{200} + \dfrac{1}{150}\right]}} = 1.10$$

    $P[Z > 1.10] = 0.1357.$
    There is no sufficient evidence to conclude that breast cancer is more prevalent in the urban community.

Section 10.13 One- and Two-Sample Tests Concerning Variances

1. H_0: $\sigma^2 = 0.03$
   H_1: $\sigma^2 \ne 0.03$

   $$\chi^2 = (9)(0.24585)^2/(0.03) = 18.13;$$
   $$2P[\chi_9^2 > 18.13] = 0.0676.$$

   The sample of 10 containers is not sufficient to show that σ^2 is not equal to 0.03.

3. H_0: $\sigma^2 = 4.2$ ppm
   H_1: $\sigma^2 \neq 4.2$ ppm

   $\chi^2 = (63)(4.25)^2/(4.2) = 63.75$;
   $2P[\chi^2_{63} > 63.75] = 0.8998$.
   The variance of aflotoxins is not significantly different from 4.2 ppm.

5. H_0: $\sigma^2 = 1.15$
   H_1: $\sigma^2 > 1.15$

   $\chi^2 = (24)(2.03)^2/(1.15) = 42.37$;
   $2P[\chi^2_{24} > 42.37] = 0.0117$.
   There is sufficient evidence to conclude that the soft drink machine is out of control.

7. H_0: $\sigma_1^2 = \sigma_2^2$
   H_1: $\sigma_1^2 > \sigma_2^2$

   $f = (6.1)^2/(5.3)^2 = 1.33$;
   $P[F_{10,13} > 1.33] = 0.3095$.
   The variability of the time to assemble the product is not significantly greater for men.

9. H_0: $\sigma_1 = \sigma_2$
   H_1: $\sigma_1 < \sigma_2$

   $f = (5100)^2/(5900)^2 = 0.747$;
   $P[F_{11,11} < 0.747] = 0.3186$.
   The standard deviations for the two brands of tires are not significantly different.

11. H_0: $\sigma_A = \sigma_B$
    H_1: $\sigma_A = \sigma_2$

    $f = (0.0125)/(0.0108) = 1.15$;
    $2P[F_{8,8} > 1.15] = 0.8452$.
    The two instruments appear to have similar variability.

13. H_0: $\sigma_1 = \sigma_2$ $s_1 = 281.0667$ (1980 models)
    H_1: $\sigma_1 \neq \sigma_2$ $s_2 = 119.3946$ (1990 models)

    $f = 5.54$ $P = 0.0005$

    Decision: Hydrocarbon emissions are more consistent in the 1990 model cars.

Section 10.18 Two-Sample Case Study

1. H_0: die is balanced.
    H_1: dies is unbalanced.
    $\alpha = 0.01$.
    Critical region: $\chi^2 > 15.086$.
    Computations: Since $e_i = 30$, $i = 1, 2, \ldots, 6$, then
    $$\chi^2 = (28 - 30)^2/30 + (36 - 30)^2/30 + \cdots + (23 - 30)^2/30$$
    $$= 4.47.$$
    Decision: Do not reject H_0; the die is balanced.

3. H_0: nuts are mixed in the ratio 5:2:2:1.
    H_1: nuts are not mixed in the ratio 5:2:2:1.
    $\alpha = 0.05$
    Critical region: $\chi^2 > 7.815$.
    Computations:

Observed	269	112	74	45
Expected	250	100	100	50

    $\chi^2 = (269 - 250)^2/250 + (112 - 100)^2/100 + (74 - 100)^2/100 + (45 - 50)^2/50 = 10.14$.
    Decision: Reject H_0; the nuts are not mixed in the ratio 5:2:2:1.

5. H_0: Data follows the binomial distribution $b(y; 3, 1/4)$, for $y = 0, 1, 2, 3$.
    H_1: Data does not follow the binomial distribution.
    $\alpha = 0.01$.
    Computations: $b(0; 3, 1/4) = 27/64$, $b(1; 3, 1/4) = 27.64$,
    $b(2; 3, 1/4) = 9/64$, $b(3; 3, 1/4) = 1/64$. Hence $e_1 = 27$, $e_2 = 27$, $e_3 = 9$, and $e_4 = 1$.

    Combining the last two classes, we find
    $\chi^2 = (21 - 27)^2/27 + (31 - 27)^2/27 + (12 - 10)^2/10 = 2.33$.
    Critical region: $\chi^2 > 9.210$.
    Decision: Do not reject H_0; the data follows the binomial distribution.

7. H_0: $f(x) = g(x; 1/2)$, for $x = 1, 2, 3, \ldots$
    H_1: $f(x) \neq g(x; 1/2)$.
    $\alpha = 0.05$.
    Computations: $g(1; 1/2) = 1/2$, $g(2; 1/2) = 1/4$, $g(3; 1/2) = 1/8$, $g(4; 1/2) = 1/16$,
    $g(5; 1/2) = 1/32$, $g(6; 1/2) = 1/64$, $g(7; 1/2) = 1/128$, $g(8; 1.2) = 1/256$.
    Now $e_1 = 128$, $e_2 = 64$, $e_3 = 32$, $e_4 = 16$, $e_5 = 8$, $e_6 = 4$, $e_7 = 2$, and $e_8 = 1$.
    Combining the last 3 classes,
    $\chi^2 = (136 - 128)^2/128 + (60 - 64)^2/64 + \cdots + (5 - 7)^2/7$
    $= 2.57$.

    Critical region: $\chi^2 > 11.070$.
    Decision: Do not reject H_0; $f(x) = g(x; 1/2)$, $x = 1, 2, 3, \ldots$

11.

z values	$P(Z < z)$	$P(z_{i-1} < Z < z_i)$	e_i	o_i
$z_1 = (0.795 - 1.8)/0.4 = -2.51$	0.0060	0.0060	0.2	1
$z_2 = (0.995 - 1.8)/0.4 = -2.01$	0.0222	0.0162	0.6	1
$z_3 = (1.195 - 1.8)/0.4 = -1.51$	0.0655	0.0433	1.7 $\}$ 6.1	1 $\}$ 5
$z_4 = (1.395 - 1.8)/0.4 = -1.01$	0.1562	0.0907	3.6	2
$z_5 = (1.595 - 1.8)/0.4 = -0.51$	0.3050	0.1488	6.0	4
$z_6 = (1.795 - 1.8)/0.4 = -0.01$	0.4960	0.1910	7.6	13
$z_7 = (1.995 - 1.8)/0.4 = 0.49$	0.6879	0.1919	7.7	8
$z_8 = (2.195 - 1.8)/0.4 = 0.99$	0.8389	0.1510	6.0	5
$z_9 = (2.395 - 1.8)/0.4 = 1.49$	0.9319	0.0930	3.7 $\}$ 6.4	3 $\}$ 5
$z_{10} = \infty$	1.0000	0.0681	2.7	2

A goodness-of-fit test with 5 degrees of freedom is based on the following data:

o_i	5	4	13	8	5	5
e_i	6.1	6.0	7.6	7.7	6.0	6.4

H_0: Distribution of nicotine contents is normal.
H_1: Distribution of nicotine contents is not normal.
$\alpha = 0.01$.
Critical region: $\chi^2 > 15.086$.
Computations: $\chi^2 = (5 - 6.1)^2/6.1 + (4 - 6.0)^2/6.0 + \cdots + (5 - 6.4)^2/6.4$
$= 5.19$.
Decision: Do not reject H_0; the distribution of nicotine contents is normal.

13. H_0: A person's gender and time spent watching television are independent.
H_1: A person's gender and time spent watching television are not independent.
$\alpha = 0.01$.
Critical region: $\chi^2 > 6.635$ for $\nu = 1$ degree-of-freedom.
Computations:

Observed and Expected Freqencies

	Male	Female	Total
Over 25 hours	15(20.5)	29(23.5)	44
Under 25 hours	27(21.5)	19(24.5)	46
Total	42	48	90

$\chi^2 = (15 - 20.5)^2/20.5 + (29 - 23.5)^2/23.5 + (27 - 21.5)^2/21.5 + (19 - 24.5)^2/24.5$
$= 5.47$.
Decision: Do not reject H_0; a person's gender and the amount of time spend watching television are independent.

15. H_0: Occurrence of types of crime is independent of city district.
H_1: Occurrence of types of crime is dependent upon city district.
$\alpha = 0.01$.
Critical region: $\chi^2 > 21.666$ for $\nu = 9$ degrees of freedom.

Observed and Expected Freqencies

District	Assault	Burglary	Larceny	Homocide	Total
1	162(186.4)	118(125.8)	451(423.5)	18(13.3)	749
2	310(380.0)	196(256.6)	996(863.4)	25(27.1)	1527
3	258(228.7)	193(154.4)	458(519.6)	10(16.3)	919
4	280(214.9)	175(145.2)	390(488.5)	19(15.3)	864
Total	1010	682	2295	72	4059

$\chi^2 = (162 - 186.4)^2/186.4 + (118 - 125.8)^2/125.8 +$
$(451 - 423.5)^2/423.5 + (18 - 13.3)^2/13.3 +$
$(310 - 380.0)^2/380.0 + (196 - 256.6)^2/256.6 +$
$(996 - 863.4)^2/863.4 + (25 - 27.1)^2/27.1 +$
$(258 - 228.7)^2 + (193 - 154.4)^2/154.4 +$
$(458 - 519.6)^2/519.6 + (10 - 16.3)^2/16.3 +$
$(280 - 214.9)^2/214.9 + (175 - 145.2)^2/145.2 +$
$(390 - 488.5)^2/488.5 + (19 - 15.3)^2/15.3$
$= 124.59.$

Decision: Reject H_0; occurrence of types of crime is dependent upon city district.

17. H_0: The attitudes among the four countries are homogenious
        H_1: The attitudes among the four countries are not homogenious

Observed and Expected Frequencies

Attitude	County				Total
	Craig	Giles	Franklin	Montgomery	
Favor	65(74.5)	66(55.9)	40(37.3)	34(37.3)	205
Oppose	42(53.5)	30(40.1)	33(26.7)	42(26.7)	147
No opinion	93(72.0)	54(54.0)	27(36.0)	24(36.0)	198
Total	200	150	100	100	550

$\chi^2 = (65 - 74.5)^2/74.5 + (66 - 55.9)^2/55.9 + (40 - 37.3)^2/37.3 +$
$(34 - 37.3)^2/37.3 + (42 - 53.5)^2/53.5 + (30 - 40.1)^2/40.1 +$
$(33 - 26.7)^2/26.7 + (42 - 26.7)^2/26.7 + (93 - 72.0)^2/72.0 +$
$(54 - 54.0)^2/54.0 + (27 - 36.0)^2/36.0 + (24 - 36.0)^2/36.0$
$= 31.17.$

$P[\chi_6^2 > 31.17] = 0.0002;$
The attitudes are not homogeneous.

19. H_0: Proportions of households within each standard of living category are equal.

    H_1: Proportions of households within each standard of living category are not equal.

    $\alpha = 0.05$.

    Critical region: $\chi^2 > 12.592$ for $v = 6$ degrees of freedom.

    Computations:

Observed and Expected Frequencies

Period	Somewhat better	Same	Not as good	Total
1980: Jan.	72(66.6)	144(145.2)	84(88.2)	300
May	63(66.6)	135(145.2)	102(88.2)	300
Sept.	47(44.4)	100(96.8)	53(58.8)	200
1981: Jan.	40(44.4)	105(96.8)	55(58.8)	200
Total	222	484	294	1000

$$\chi^2 = (72 - 66.6)^2/66.6 + (144 - 145.2)^2/145.2 + (84 - 88.2)^2/88.2$$
$$+ (63 - 66.6)^2/66.6 + (135 - 145.2)^2/145.2 +$$
$$(102 - 88.2)^2/88.2 + (47 - 44.4)^2/44.4 = (100 - 96.8)^2/96.8$$
$$+ (53 - 58.8)^2/58.8 + (40 - 44.4)^2/44.4 + (105 - 96.8)^2/96.8$$
$$+ (55 - 58.8)^2/58.8$$
$$= 5.92.$$

$P[\chi_6^2 > 5.92] = 0.4322;$

The proportions within each standard of living category appear to be equal.

21. H_0: Proportions of voters favoring candidate A, candidate B, or undecided are the same for each city.

    H_1: Proportions of voters favoring candidate A, candidate B, or undecided are not the same for each city.

    $\alpha = 0.05$.

    Critical region: $\chi^2 > 5.991$ for $v = 2$ degrees of freedom.

    Computations:

Observed and Expected Frequencies

	Richmond	Norfolk	Total
Favor A	204(214.5)	225(214.5)	429
Favor B	211(204.5)	198(204.5)	409
Undecided	85(81)	77(81)	162
Total	500	500	1000

$$\chi^2 = (204 - 214.5)^2/214.5 + (225 - 214.5)^2/214.5 +$$
$$(211 - 204.5)^2/204.5 + (198 - 204.5)^2/204.5 +$$
$$(85 - 81)^2/81 + (77 - 81)^2/81$$
$$= 1.84.$$

Decision: Do not reject H_0; the proportions are the same.

Chapter 11
Simple Linear Regression and Correlation

Section 11.3 Least Squares and the Fitted Model

1. (a) $\sum x = 778.7$, $\sum y = 2050.0$, $\sum x^2 = 26{,}591.63$, $\sum xy = 65{,}164.04$, $n = 25$.
    Therefore

    $$b = \frac{(25)(65{,}164.04) - (778.7)(2050)}{(25)(26{,}591.63) - (778.7)^2} = 0.56089779,$$
    $$a = [2050 - (0.56089779)(778.7)]/25 = 64.52915564.$$

    (b) Using the equation $\hat{y} = 64.52916 + 0.56090x$ with $x = 30$,
    we find $\hat{y} = 64.52916 + (0.56090)(30) = 81.4$.

    (c) Residuals appear to be random as desired.

3. (a) $\sum x = 16.5$, $\sum y = 100.4$, $\sum x^2 = 25.85$, $\sum xy = 152.59$, $n = 11$.
    Therefore

    $$b = \frac{(11)(152.59) - (16.5)(100.4)}{(11)(25.85) - (16.5)^2} = 1.8090909,$$
    $$a = [100.4 - (1.8090909)(16.5)]/11 = 6.4136364.$$
    Hence, $\hat{y} = 6.4136 + 1.8091x$.

    (b) For $x = 1.75$, $\hat{y} = 6.4136 + (1.8091)(1.75) = 9.580$.

    (c) Residuals appear to be random as desired.

5. (a) $\sum x = 675$, $\sum y = 488$, $\sum x^2 = 37{,}125$, $\sum xy = 25{,}005$, $n = 18$.
    Therefore

    $$b = \frac{(18)(25{,}005) - (675)(488)}{(18)(37{,}125) - (675)^2} = 0.5676190,$$
    $$a = [488 - (0.567619)(675)]/18 = 5.8253986.$$
    Hence, $\hat{y} = 5.8254 + 0.5676x$.

(b)

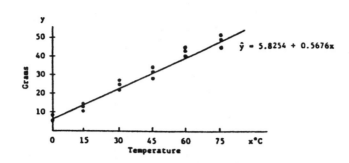

(c) For x = 50, y = 5.8254 + (0.5676)(50) = 34.205 grams.

7.   (a)

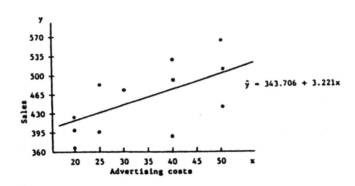

(b) $\sum x = 410$, $\sum y = 5445$, $\sum x^2 = 15{,}650$, $\sum xy = 191{,}325$, n = 12. Therefore

$$b = \frac{(12)(191{,}325) - (410)(5445)}{(12)(15{,}650) - (410)^2} = 3.22081218.$$

a = [5445 − (3.22081218)(410)]/12 = 343.705584.

Hence, $\hat{y} = 343.706 + 3.221x$. See plotted line in 7(a).

(c) When x = $35, $\hat{y} = 343.706 + (3.221)(35) = \$456$.

(d) Residuals appear to be random as desired.

9.   (a) $\sum x = 45$, $\sum y = 1094$, $\sum x^2 = 244.26$, $\sum y^2 = 133.786$, $\sum xy = 5348.2$, n = 9. Therefore

$$b = \frac{(9)(5348.2) - (45)(1094)}{(9)(244.26) - (45)^2} = -6.3239875,$$

a = [1094 − (−6.3239875)(45)]/9 = 153.17549.
Hence, $\hat{y} = 153{,}175 - 6.324x$.

(b) For x = 4.8, $\hat{y} = 153.175 - (6.324)(4.8) = 123$.

Section 11.6 Prediction

1. The least squares estimator A of α is a linear combination of normally distributed random variables and is thus normal.

$$E(A) = E(\bar{Y} - B\bar{x}) = E(\bar{Y}) - \bar{x}E(B)$$
$$= \alpha + \beta\bar{x} - \beta\bar{x} = \alpha.$$
$$\sigma_A^2 = \sigma_{\bar{Y}}^2 = B\bar{x}$$
$$= \sigma_{\bar{Y}}^2 + \bar{x}^2\sigma_B^2 - 2\bar{x}\sigma_{\bar{Y}B}$$
$$= \frac{\sigma^2}{n} + \frac{\bar{x}^2\sigma^2}{\sum_{i=1}^{n}(x_i - \bar{x})^2}, \text{ since } \sigma_{\bar{Y}B} = 0.$$

Hence

$$\sigma_A^2 = \frac{\sum_{i=1}^{n}x_i^2}{n\sum_{i=1}^{n}(x_i - \bar{x})^2}\sigma^2.$$

3. $S_{xx} = 26{,}591.63 - 778.7^2/25 = 2336.6824,$
$S_{yy} = 172{,}891.46 - 2050^2/25 = 4791.46,$
$S_{xy} = 65{,}164.04 - (778.7)(2050)/25 = 1310.64,$
$b = 0.56090.$
   (a) $s^2 = [4791.46 - (0.56090)(1310.64)]/23 = 176.362.$
   (b) H_0: $\beta = 0.$
   H_1: $\beta \neq 0.$
   $\alpha = 0.05.$
   Critical region: $t < -2.069$ and $t > 2.069.$
   Computations:
   $$t = \frac{0.56090}{\sqrt{176.362/2336.6824}} = 2.04.$$

   Decision: Do not reject H_0.

5. $S_{xx} = 25.85 - 16.5^2/11 = 1.1,$
$S_{yy} = 923.58 - 100.4^2/11 = 7.2018,$
$S_{xy} = 152.59 - (165)(100.4)/11 = 1.99,$
$a = 6.4136$ and $b = 1.8091.$
   (a) $s^2 = [7.2018 - (1.8091)(1.99)]/9 = 0.40.$
   (b) Since $s = 0.632$ and $t_{0.025} = 2.262$ with $v = 9$ degrees of freedom, then
   $$6.4136 - (2.262)(0.632)\sqrt{25.85}/\sqrt{(11)(1.1)} < \alpha$$
   $$< 6.4136 + (2.262)(0.632)\sqrt{25.85}/\sqrt{(11)(1.1)} \text{ ; or}$$
   $$4.324 < \alpha < 8.503$$
   (c) $1.8091 - (2.262)(0.632)/\sqrt{(1.1)} < \beta < 1.8091 + (2.262)(0.632)/\sqrt{(1.1)} \text{ ; or}$
   $$0.446 < \beta < 3.172$$

7. $S_{xx} = 37{,}125 - 675^2/18 = 11{,}812.5,$
    $S_{yy} = 17{,}142 - 488^2/18 = 3911.7778,$
    $S_{xy} = 25{,}005 - (675)(488)/18 = 6705,$
    $a = 5.8254$ and $b = 0.5676.$

    (a) $s^2 = [3911.7778 - (0.5676)(6705)]/16 = 6.626.$

    (b) Since $s = 2.574$ and $t_{0.005} = 2.921$ with $\nu = 16$ degrees of freedom, then
    $$5.8261 - (2.921)(2.574)\sqrt{37{,}125}\,/\sqrt{(18)(11{,}812.5)} < \alpha$$
    $$< 5.8261 + (2.921)(2.574)\sqrt{37{,}125}\,/\sqrt{(18)(11{,}812.5)}$$
    which simplifies to
    $$2.684 < \alpha < 8.968.$$

    (c) $0.5676 - (2.921)(2.574)/\sqrt{11{,}812.5} < \beta < 0.5676 + (2.921)(2.574)/\sqrt{11{,}812.5}$
    or
    $$0.498 < \beta < 0.637.$$

9. H_0: $\beta = 6.$
    H_1: $\beta < 6.$
    $\alpha = 0.025.$
    Critical region: $t < -2.228.$
    Computations: $S_{xx} = 15{,}650 - 410^2/12 = 1641.667,$
    $\qquad\qquad\qquad S_{yy} = 2{,}512{,}925 - 5445^2/12 = 42256.25,$
    $\qquad\qquad\qquad S_{xy} = 191{,}325 - (410)(5445)/12 = 5287.5,$
    $\qquad\qquad\qquad s^2 = [42256.25 - (3.221)(5287.5)]/10$
    $\qquad\qquad\qquad\quad = 2522.521$ and then $s = 50.225.$ Now,
    $$t = \frac{3.221 - 6}{50.225/\sqrt{1641.667}} = -2.24.$$
    Decision: Reject H_0, $\beta < 6.$

11. Using the value $s = 1.64$ from Exercise 6(a) and the fact that $y_0 = 25{,}7724$ when $x_0 = 24.5$ and $\bar{x} = 25.9667$, we have

    (a) $25.7724 - (2.228)(1.640)\sqrt{1/12 + (-1.4667)^2/43.0467} < \mu_{Y/24.5}$
    $$< 25.7724 + (2.228)(1.640)\sqrt{1/12 + (-1.4667)^2/43.0467} \, ;$$
    Simplifying, $24.438 < \mu_{Y|24.5} < 27.106.$

    (b) $25.7724 - (2.228)(1.640)\sqrt{1 + 1/12 + (-1.4667)^2/43.0467} < y_0$
    $$< 25.7724 + (2.228)(1.640)\sqrt{1 + 1/12 + (-1.4667)^2/43.0467} \, ;$$
    Simplifying, $21.883 < y_0 < 29.662.$

13. Using the value $s = 0.632$ from Exercise 5(a) and the fact that
    $y_0 = 9.308$ when $x_0 = 1.6$, and $\bar{x} = 1.5$, we have,
    $$9.308 - (2.262)(0.632)\sqrt{1 + 1/11 + (0.1)^2/1.1} < y_0$$
    $$< 9.308 < (2.262)(0.632)\sqrt{1 + 1/11 + (0.1)^2/1.1} \, ;$$
    Simplifying, $7{,}815 < y_0 < 10.801.$

15.   (a) 17.1812.

       (b) The goal of 30 mpg is unlikely based on the confidence interval for mean mpg, [27.95, 29.60].

       (c) Based on the prediction interval the Lexus ES300 should exceed 18 mpg.

Section 11.9 Test for Linearity of Regression: Data with Repeated Observations

1.   (a) Find b which minimizes $\sum_{i=1}^{n}(y_i - bx_i)^2 = SSE$.

$$\frac{\partial(SSE)}{\partial b} = -2\sum_{i=1}^{n}(y_i - bx_i)x_i.$$

Equating to zero, and solving for b we have the estimate

$$b = \sum_{i=1}^{n}x_i y_i \bigg/ \sum x_i^2.$$

       (b) $\sum x_i y_i = 197.59, \qquad \sum x_i^2 = 98.64.$

Therefore $b = 197.59/98.64 = 2.003$ and $\hat{y} = 2.003x$.

3. $E(B) = \dfrac{1}{\sum_{i=1}^{n}(x_{1i} - \bar{x}_1)^2}\left[\sum_{i=1}^{n}(x_{1i} - \bar{x}_1)E(Y_i)\right]$

$$= \dfrac{1}{\sum_{i=1}^{n}(x_{1i} - \bar{x}_1)^2}\left[\sum_{i=1}^{n}(x_{1i} - \bar{x}_1)(\alpha + \beta x_{1i} + \gamma x_{2i})\right]$$

$$= \dfrac{1}{\sum_{i=1}^{n}(x_{1i} - \bar{x}_1)^2}\left[\beta\sum_{i=1}^{n}(x_{1i} - \bar{x}_1)^2 + \gamma\sum_{i=1}^{n}(x_{1i} - \bar{x}_1)x_{2i}\right]$$

$$= \beta + \dfrac{\gamma\sum_{i=1}^{n}(x_{1i} - \bar{x}_1)x_{2i}}{\sum_{i=1}^{n}(x_{1i} - \bar{x}_1)^2}$$

5.   (a) $S_{xx} = 2248.25 - 172.5^2/25 = 1058$,

$S_{yy} = 1979.60 - 211^2/25 = 198.76$,

$S_{xy} = 1092.27 - (172.5)(211)/25 = -363.63$,

$b = S_{xy}/S_{xx} = -363.63/1058 = -0.34370$

$a = [211 - (-0.34370)(172.5)]/25 = 10.81153$.

       (b) H_0: The regression is linear in x.

H_1: The regression is nonlinear in x.

$\alpha = 0.05$

Critical region: $f > 3.10$ with 3 and 20 degrees of freedom.

Computations: We have

SST = S_{yy} = 198.76,

SSR = bS_{xy} = S_{xy}^2/S_{xx} = $(-363.63)^2/1058$ = 124.98,

SSE = $S_{yy} - bS_{xy}$ = 73.78, and with T_1 = 51.1,

T_2 = 51.5, T_3 = 49.3, T_4 = 37.0, T_5 = 22.1,

$$SSE(pure) = \sum_{i=1}^{5}\sum_{j=1}^{5} y_{ij}^2 - \sum_{i=1}^{5} T_{i.}^2/5$$

$$= 1979.60 - 1910.272 = 69.33,$$

Lack of fit SS = 73.78 − 69.33 = 4.45.

Source of Variation	Sum of Squares	Degrees of Freedom	Mean Square	Computed f
Regression	124.98	1	124.98	
Lack of fit	4.45	3	1.48	0.43
Pure error	69.33	20	3.47	
Total	198.76	24		

Decision: Do not reject H_0.

7. H_0: The regression is linear.

H_1: The regression is nonlinear.

α = 0.05.

Critical region: f > 3.00 with 6 and 12 degrees of freedom.

SST = S_{yy} = 5928.55,

SSR = bS_{xy} = S_{xy}^2/S_{xx} = $(2588.5)^2/5495$ = 1219.35,

SSE = $S_{yy} - bS_{xy}$ = 4709.20,

$$SSE(pure) = \sum_{i=1}^{8}\sum_{j=1}^{n_i} y_{ij}^2 - \sum_{i=1}^{8} T_{i.}^2/n_i$$

$$= 74.725 - 71704.33 = 3020.67,$$

Lack of fit SS = 4709.20 − 3020.67 = 1688.53.

Source of Variation	Sum of Squares	Degrees of Freedom	Mean Square	Computed f
Regression	1219.35	1	1219.35	
Lack of fit	1688.53	6	281.42	1.12
Pure error	3020.67	12	251.72	
Total	5928.55	19		

The lack-of-fit test was insignificant.

9. $\hat{y}$ = −21.0280 + 0.4072x;

f_{LOF} = 1.71; P[F > 1.71] = 0.2517; Lack-of-fit is insignificant.

The linear model is adequate.

11.   (a) $\hat{y} = -11.3251 - 0.0449$ temperature;

      (b)   Yes;

      (c)   0.9355;

      (d)   The proportion of impurities does depend on temperature.
Based on the plot that follows it does not appear to be a linear dependence.
If there were replicates a lack-of-fit test could be performed.

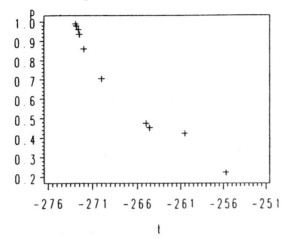

13.   (a)

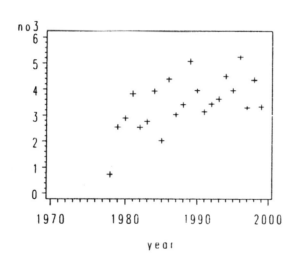

      (b) $\hat{y} = -175.9025 + 0.0902$ year;

      (c)   There is definitely a relationship between year and nitrogen oxide. It does not appear to be linear.

Section 11.12 Correlation

1. $S_{xx} = 36,354 - 35,882.667 = 471.333,$
$S_{yy} = 38,254 - 37,762.667 = 491.333.$
$S_{xy} = 36,926 - 36,810.667 = 115.333.$

3. Since $b = S_{xy}/S_{xx}$, we can write

$$s^2 = (S_{yy} - bS_{xy})/(n-2) = (S_{yy} - b^2S_{xx})/(n-2).$$

We can also write $b = r\sqrt{S_{yy}S_{xx}}$ so that

$$s^2 = (S_{yy} - r^2S_{yy})/(n-2) = S_{yy}(1-r^2)/(n-2),$$

and hence

$$t = \frac{b}{s\sqrt{S_{xx}}} = \frac{r\sqrt{S_{yy}/S_{xx}}}{\sqrt{S_{yy}S_{xx}(1-r^2)/(n-2)}} = \frac{r\sqrt{n-2}}{\sqrt{1-r^2}}.$$

5. (a) From the data of Exercise 1 on page 48 of this manual we can calculate
$S_{xx} = 26{,}591.63 - (778.7)^2/25 = 2336.6824$;
$S_{yy} = 172{,}891.46 - (2050)^2/25 = 4791.46$;
$S_{xy} = 65{,}164.04 - (778.7)(2050)/25 = 1310.64$; Therefore,

$$r = \frac{1310.64}{\sqrt{(2336.6824)(4791.46)}} = 0.392.$$

(b) H_0: $\rho = 0$.
H_a: $\rho \neq 0$.
$\alpha = 0.05$.
Critical region: $t < -2.069$ and $t > 2.069$.
Computations:

$$t = \frac{0.392\sqrt{23}}{\sqrt{1-0.392^2}} = 2.04.$$

P-value = 0.0530; ρ is significantly different from 0 at the $\alpha = 0.053$ level.

Chapter 12
Multiple Linear Regression and Certain Nonlinear Regression Models

Section 12.3 Linear Regression Model Using Matrices

1. (a) From the computer printout we find the least squares estimates $b_0 = 27.547$, $b_1 = 0.922$, and $b_2 = 0.284$. Therefore, our fitted regression equation is

$$\hat{y} = 27.547 + 0.922x_1 + 0.284x_2.$$

 (b) When $x_1 = 60$ and $x_2 = 4$, we estimate the chemistry grade to be

$$\hat{y} = 27.547 + (0.922)(60) + (0.284)(4) = 84.$$

3. From the computer printout we find the least squares esitmates $b_0 = 0.5800$, $b_1 = 2.7122$, and $b_2 = 2.0497$. Therefore,
$$\hat{y} = 0.5800 + 2.7122x_1 + 2.0497x_2.$$

5. (a) From the computer printout with $x_1 - x$ and $x_2 = x^2$, we find the least squares estimates $b_0 = 56.4633$, $b_1 = 0.1525$, and $b_2 = -0.00008$. Therefore, the fitted equation is

$$\hat{y} = 56.4633 + 0.1525x - 0.00008x^2.$$

 (b) When $x = 225°C$, we estimate the yield to be

$$\hat{y} = 56.4633 + (0.1525)(225) - (0.00008)(225^2) = 86.7\%.$$

7. From the computer printout with $x_1 = x$ and $x_2 = x^2$, we find $b_0 = 141.6188$, $b_1 = -0.2819$, and $b_2 = 0.0003$. Therefore,

$$\hat{y} = 141.6118 - 0.2819x + 0.0003x^2.$$

9. (a) $\hat{y} = -102.7132 + 0.6054x_1 + 8.9236x_2 + 1.4374x_3 + 0.0136x_4.$
 (b) $\hat{y} = 287.6.$

11. From the computer printout $\hat{y} = 3.3205 + 0.4210x_1 - 0.2958x_2 + 0.0164x_3 + 0.1247x_4.$

13. From the computer printout $\hat{y} = -6.5122 + 1.9994x_1 - 3.6751x_2 + 2.5245x_3$
$$+ 5.1581x_4 + 14.4012x_5$$

15. (a) $\hat{y} = 350.9943 - 1.2720x_1 - 0.1539x_2.$
 (b) $\hat{y}_{20,1200} = 140.9.$

Section 12.5 Inferences in Multiple Linear Regression

1. $s^2 = 0.1651$.

3. $s^2 = 242.7156$.

5.   From Exercise 3 we have $s^2 = 242.7156$. The pertinent elements of A^{-1} given in the computer printout are $c_{22} = 0.115755$, and $c_{14} = -0.00003948$.

    (a) $\hat{\sigma}^2_{\beta_2} = c_{22}s^2 = (0.115755)(242.7156) = 28.0955$.

    (b) $\hat{\sigma}_{\beta_1\beta_4} = c_{14}s^2 = (-0.00003948)(242.7156) = -0.009582$.

7.   For $x = 19.5$ we find $\hat{y}_0 = 30.9506$. Next we find $x'_0 A^{-1} x_0 = 0.16062$. From the computer printout we have $s^2 = 2.04$. Now, $t_{0.05} = 1.782$ with 12 degrees of freedom, and then

$$30.9506 - 1.782\sqrt{(2.04)(0.16062)} < \mu_{Y|19.5} < 30.9506$$

which simplifies to

$$29.93 < \mu_{Y|19.5} < 31.97.$$

9. H_0: $\beta_2 = 0$
H_1: $\beta_2 \neq 0$
$\alpha = 0.05$.
Critical region: $t < -2.179$ and $t > 2.179$.
Computations:
    $b_2 = 0.00030914$, $s = 2.979$, and $c_{22} = 1.3201476 \times 10^{-9}$.

$$t = \frac{0.00030914}{2.979\sqrt{1.3201476 \times 10^{-9}}} = 2.86.$$

Decision: Reject H_0: $\beta_2 > 0$.

11. H_0: $\beta_1 = 2$
H_1: $\beta_2 \neq 2$
$\alpha = 0.05$
Critical region: $t < -2.365$ and $t > 2.365$.
Computations:
$t = (b_1 - 2.0)\sqrt{\hat{\sigma}^2_{\beta_1}} = (2.7122 - 2.0)/0.2007 = 3.55$.
Decision: Reject H_0: $P = 0.01$

13.   (a) $t = -1.09$; $P[T < -1.09] + P[T > 1.09] = 0.3562$;
    (b) $t = -1.72$; $P[T < -1.72] + P[T > 1.72] = 0.1841$;
    (c)   Yes; neither x_1 nor x_2 is significant in this model.

Section 12.7 Special Case of Orthogonality

1. $SSR = (0.5800)(489.15) + (2.7122)(3875.9365) + (2.0497)(11,749.8781) - (489.15)^2/10$
    $= 10,952.97.$
    $SST = 34,882.9961 - (489.15)^2/10 = 10,956.22.$

    Therefore, $R^2 = \dfrac{SSR}{SST} = \dfrac{10,952.97}{10,956.22} = 0.9997,$

    so that 99.97% of the variation of the Y values in our sample is explained by the linear model.

3. $f_{4,7} = 5.106;\ P[F > 5.106] = 0.0303.$
    This regression model is significant at the 0.03 level.

5. $f_{1,9} = \dfrac{(7.2484 - 1.4857)/1}{0.1651} = 34.90;\ P[F > 34.90] = 0.00025.$
    Decision: Reject H_0; X_1 is significant in the presence of X_2.

7. $f_{2,7} = \dfrac{(6639.2266 - 1699.0093)/2}{242.7156}$ and 10.18; $P[F > 10.18] = 0.0085.$
    Decision: Reject H_0; X_1 and X_2 are significant in the presence of X_3 and X_4.

9. s^2 for the model using weight alone is 8.1271.
    s^2 for the model using weight and drive ratio is 4.7802.
    Both variables are significant.
    The two variable model is better.

Section 12.8 Categorical or Indicator Variables

1. (a) $\hat{y} = 5.9593 - 0.00003773$ odometer $+ 0.3374$ octane $- 12.6266$ van $- 12.9846$ suv;
    (b) sedan
    (c) The parameter estimates are less than one standard error apart. There is no significant difference.

Variable	DF	Parameter Estimate	Standard Error	t Value	Pr > |t|
Intercept	1	5.95931	7.05751	0.84	0.4084
odometer	1	-0.00003773	0.00001593	-2.37	0.0281
octane	1	0.33735	0.08380	4.03	0.0007
z1	1	-12.62656	1.07219	-11.78	<.0001
z2	1	-12.98455	1.11483	-11.65	<.0001

Section 12.11 Cross Validation, C_p, and Other Criteria for Model Selection

1. (a) From the computer printout we find the least squares estimates $b_0 = 1.10765$,
    $b_2 = 0.01370$, and $b_5 = 0.00429$. Therefore,

    $\hat{y} = 1.10765 + 0.01370x_2 + 0.00429x_5.$

(b) When $x_2 = 180$ lbs. and $x_5 = 260$ ft. lbs., the predicted hang time is

$$\hat{y} = 1.10765 + (0.01370)(180) + (0.00429)(260) = 4.690 \text{ seconds.}$$

(c) Writing $\underline{x}_0' = [1, 180, 260]$ and reading the elements of $\underline{A}^{-1}$ from the computer printout, we find

$$\underline{x}_0' \underline{A}^{-1} \underline{x}_0 = 0.31399$$

and hence with $\hat{y} = 4.690$ and $s^2 = 0.03691$, we get

$$4.690 - (2.228)\sqrt{(0.03291)(0.31399)} < \mu_{Y|180,260}$$
$$< 4.690 + (2.228)\sqrt{(0.03691)(0.31399)}$$

which simplifies to

$$4.450 < \mu_{Y|180,260} < 4.930.$$

3. We find $R(\beta_4 \mid \beta_1, \beta_2, \beta_4) = 0.024148$ to be the smallest adjusted regression sum of squares. Now,

$$f = 0.024148/0.7414 = 0.033,$$

which is not significant. hence x_4 is removed from the equation. With the combination of variables (x_1, x_2, x_3) we find that x_1 contributes the least to the regression in the presence of x_2 and x_3. Now, $R(\beta_1 \mid \beta_2, \beta_3) = 0.046669$ and $f = 0.046669 \div 0.5975 = 0.078$ and x_1 is removed. In the next step both x_2 and x_3 are significant at the 0.05 level since $R(\beta_2 \mid \beta_3) = 132.0971$ with $f = 132.0971/0.50606 = 261$ and $R(\beta_3 \mid \beta_2) = 102.90229$ with $f = 102.90229/0.50606 = 203.33761$. Hence, the final equation is

$$\hat{y} = 2.1833 + 0.9576x_2 + 3.3253x_3.$$

5. (a) The computer printout gives $b_0 = -587.211$ and $b_1 = 428.433$. Therefore,
$$\hat{y} = -587.211 + 428.433x.$$

(b) The computer printout gives $b_0 = 1180$, $b_1 = -191.691$, and $b_{11} = 35.20945$. Therefore,
$$\hat{y} = 1180 - 191.691x + 35.20945x^2.$$

(c) Linear model: $s^2 = 1{,}105{,}054$, $R^2 = 0.84$, PRESS = 18,811,057.
Quadratic model: $s^2 = 430{,}712$, $R^2 = 0.94$, PRESS = 8,706,974.
Based upon these values, we would choose the quadratic model.

7. From the computer printout we have $c_{11} = 0.04779999$, $c_{22} = .00014545728$, $c_{12} = -0.002561858$ and $s^2 = 430712.18$. Therefore,

$$\hat{\sigma}^2_{\beta_1} = (0.04779999)(430712.18) = 20{,}588.04;$$

$$\hat{\sigma}^2_{\beta_{11}} = (1.4545728)(430712.18) = 62.6502;$$

$$\hat{\sigma}^2_{\beta_1 \beta_{11}} = (-0.002561858)(430712.18) = -1103.42328.$$

9. The intercept model is best.

11. (a) $\hat{y} = 3.1368 + 0.6444x_1 - 0.0104x_2 + 0.5046x_3 - 0.1197x_4 - 2.4618x_5 + 1.5044x_6$.
    (b) $\hat{y} = 4.6563 + 0.5113x_3 - 0.1242x_4$.
    (d) $\hat{y} = 4.6563 + 0.5113x_3 - 0.1242x_4$.

    The model including x_1, x_3, and x_4 has a slightly smaller x^2 and consequently a slightly larger adjusted R^2 than the model using only x_3 and x_4. The C_p-statistic was better with the two variable model. In the three variable model the variable x_1 has a P-value of 0.30. The two variable model is better.

    (e) Observations 2 and 14 have R-Student values above 2 in absolute value. These observations should be checked.

13. (a) $\hat{y} = 125.8655 + 7.7586x_1 + 0.0943x_2 - 0.0092x_1x_2$;

    (b) The model with x_2 alone has the smallest PRESS and Cp statistic. The three variable model has the smallest s^2. The three variable model has no significant variables and a large C_p and PRESS statistic. The model with x_2 alone is best.

Chapter 13
One-Factor Experiments: General

Section 13.4 Tests for the Equality of Several Variances

1. $$SSE = \sum_{i=1}^{k}\sum_{j=1}^{n}(Y_{ij} - \bar{Y}_{i.})^2 = \sum_{i=1}^{k}\sum_{j=1}^{n}(E_{ij} - \bar{E}_{i.})^2$$

$$= \sum_{i=1}^{k}\left[\sum_{j=1}^{n}E_{ij}^2 - n\bar{E}_{i.}^2\right]$$

$$E(SSE) = \sum_{i=1}^{k}\left[\sum_{j=1}^{n}E(E_{ij}^2 - nE(\bar{E}_{i.}^2)\right]$$

$$= \sum_{i=1}^{k}[n\sigma^2 - n(\sigma^2/n)] = k(n-1)\sigma^2.$$

Therefore
$$E[SSE/k(n-1)] = k(n-1)\sigma^2/k(n-1) = \sigma^2.$$

3. H_0: $\mu_1 = \mu_2 = \cdots = \mu_6$.
H_1: At least two of the means are not equal.
$\alpha = 0.05$.
Critical region: $f > 2.77$ with $\nu_1 = 5$ and $\nu_2 = 18$ degrees of freedom.
Computations:

Source of Variation	Sum of Squares	Degrees of Freedom	Mean Square	Computed f
Treatments	5.34	5	1.07	0.31
Error	62.64	18	3.48	
Total	67.98	23		

$P = 0.9005$ Decision: The treatment means do not differ significantly.

5. H_0: $\mu_1 = \mu_2 = \mu_3$.
H_1: At least two of the means are not equal.
$\alpha = 0.01$.

Source of Variation	Sum of Squares	Degrees of Freedom	Mean Square	Computed f
Shelf height	399.3	2	199.65	14.52
Error	288.7	21	13.75	
Total	688.0	23		

$P = 0.0001$ Decision: Reject H_0. The amount of money spend on dog food differs with the shelf height of the display.

7. H_0: $\mu_1 = \mu_2 = \mu_3 = \mu_4$.
    H_1: At least two of the means are not equal.
    $\alpha = 0.05$.

Source of Variation	Sum of Squares	Degrees of Freedom	Mean Square	Computed f
Treatments	119.787	3	39.929	2.25
Error	638.248	36	17.729	
Total	758.035	39		

$P = 0.0992$ Decision: H_0 can not be rejected at the 0.05 level of significance.

The mean change in height is not significantly different for the levels of $MgNH_4PO_4$ at the alpha = 0.05 level. Based on the means and a P-value of 0.0992 it appears that 400 would be best level to use.

9. H_0: $\mu_1 = \mu_2 = \mu_3 = \mu_4$.
    H_1: At least two of the means are not equal.
    $\alpha = 0.01$.

Source of Variation	Sum of Squares	Degrees of Freedom	Mean Square	Computed f
Treatments	27.5506	3	9.1835	8.38
Error	18.6359	17	1.0962	
Total	46.1865	20		

P-value = 0.0012.   Reject H_0. Average specific activities differ.

Section 13.7 Comparing Treatments with a Control

1.

Source of Variation	Sum of Squares	Degrees of Freedom	Mean Square	Computed f
B vs A, C, D	30.6735	1	30.6735	14.27
C vs A, D	49.9230	1	49.9230	23.23
A vs D	5.3290	1	5.3290	2.48
Error	34.3800	16	2.1488	

(a) P = 0.0016   B is significantly different from the average of A, C, and D
(b) P = 0.0001   C is significantly differently from the average of A and D
(c) P = 0.1349   A can not be shown to differ significantly from D.

Not significantly different than D.

3. (a) H_0: $\mu_1 = \mu_2 = \mu_3 = \mu_4$.
        H_1: At least two of the means are not equal.
        $\alpha = 0.01$.
        Critical region: $f > 4.27$ with $\nu_1 = 3$ and $\nu_2 = 44$ degrees of freedom.

    Computations:

Source of Variation	Sum of Squares	Degrees of Freedom	Mean Square	Computed f
Treatments	1083.6006	3	361.2002	13.50
Error	1177.6792	44	26.7654	
Total	2261.2798	47		

    $P < 0.0001$ Decision: Reject H_0:. The treatment means are different.

    (b) H_0' : $\mu_1 - \mu_2 = 0$
        H_0'' : $\mu_3 - \mu_4 = 0$
        H_1' : $\mu_1 - \mu_2 \neq 0$
        H_1'' : $\mu_3 - \mu_4 \neq 0$
        $\alpha = 0.01$
        Critical region: $f > 7.26$ with $\nu_1 = 1$ and $\nu_2 = 44$ degrees of freedom
        Computations:

Contrast	Sum of Squares	Computed f
1 vs 2	785.4704	29.35
3 vs 4	96.000	3.59

    $P < 0.0001$ Bath I and bath II were different for 5 launderings.

    $P = 0.0647$ Bath I and bath II were not different for 10 launderings at the .01 level of significance.

5. $\bar{y}_1 = 59.66$, $\bar{y}_2 = 61.96$, $\bar{y}_3, = 56.52$, $\bar{y}_4 = 61.12$, $\sqrt{s^2/n} = \sqrt{2.1488/5} = 0.656$.

p	2	3	4
r_p	4.131	4.309	4.425
R_p	2.710	2.827	2.903

    The means my then be grouped as follows:

$\bar{y}_3$	$\bar{y}_1$	$\bar{y}_4$	$\bar{y}_2$
56.52	59.66	61.12	61.96

7. (a) H_0: $\mu_1 = \mu_2 = \mu_3 = \mu_4 = \mu_5$.
H_1: At least two of the means are not equal.
$\alpha = 0.01$.

Source of Variation	Sum of Squares	Degrees of Freedom	Mean Square	Computed f
Procedures	7828.3	4	1975.075	9.01
Error	3256.5	15	217.100	
Total	11084.8	19		

$P = 0.0006$. Decision: Reject H_0. There is a significant difference in the average species count for the different procedures.

(b) $\bar{y}_1 = 64.25$, $\bar{y}_2 = 55.50$, $\bar{y}_3, = 24.25$, $\bar{y}_4 = 26.50$, $\bar{y}_5 = 12.50$, and $\sqrt{s^2/n}$
$= \sqrt{217.1/4} = 7.367$.

p	2	3	4	5
r_p	3.014	3.160	3.250	3.312
R_p	22.20	23.28	23.94	24.40

The means my then be grouped as follows:

$\bar{y}_5$	$\bar{y}_3$	$\bar{y}_4$	$\bar{y}_2$	$\bar{y}_1$
12.50	24.25	26.50	55.50	64.25

9. We find $\bar{y}_0 = 6.14$, $\bar{y}_1 = 8.82$, $\bar{y}_2 = 8.16$, $\bar{y}_3 = 6.82$, and $\bar{y}_4 = 6.88$. The error mean square is found to be $s^2 = 0.2174$, and then $\sqrt{2s^2/n} = \sqrt{(2)(0.2174)/5} = 0.2949$.

Hence,

$d_1 = (8.82 - 6.14)/0.2949 = 9.0878$,
$d_2 = (8.16 - 6.14)/0.2949 = 6.8498$,
$d_3 = (6.82 - 6.14)/0.2949 = 2.3059$,
$d_4 = (6.88 - 6.14)/0.2949 = 2.5093$.

Since $d_{0.05}(4, 20) = 2.30$, the mean growths of this type of plant are all significantly larger for the four different chemical concentrations than the mean growth when no chemical is used.

11.

Source of Variation	DF	Sum of Squares	Mean Square	F-value	P-Value
Temperature	4	1268.5333	317.1333	70.27	<0.0001
Error	25	112.8333	4.5133		
Total	29	1381.3667			

Duncan Groupings

Temperature	50	75	100	25	0
Mean	72.833	70.500	64.167	60.167	55.167

$$\underline{\qquad\qquad\qquad}\qquad\qquad\underline{\qquad}$$
$$\underline{\qquad}$$
$$\underline{\qquad}$$

Batteries activated at temperatures 50 and 75 have significantly longer activated life.

13. Aggregate 4 has a significantly lower absorption rate than the other aggregates.

Section 13.11 Latin Squares

1. $$SSB = \sum_{j=1}^{b}(\bar{y}_{.j} - \bar{y}_{..})^2 = k\sum_{j=1}^{b}\left(\frac{T_{.j}}{k} - \frac{T_{..}}{bk}\right)^2$$
$$= \sum_{j=1}^{b}\frac{T_{.j}^2}{k} - 2\frac{T_{..}^2}{k} - \frac{T_{..}^2}{bk}$$
$$= \sum_{j=1}^{b}\frac{T_{.j}^2}{k} - \frac{T_{..}^2}{bk}.$$

3. (a) H_0: $\alpha_1 = \alpha_2 = \alpha_3 = \alpha_4 = 0$. (fertilizer effects are zero)
     H_1: At least one of the α_i's is not equal to zero.
     $\alpha = 0.05$.
     Critical region: $f > 4.76$;
     Computations:

Source of Variation	Sum of Squares	Degrees of Freedom	Mean Square	Computed f
Fertilizers	218.19	3	72.73	6.11
Blocks	197.63	2	98.82	
Error	71.41	6	11.90	
Total	487.23	11		

$P = 0.0296$.   Decision: Reject H_0. The means are not all equal.

(b)

Source of Variation	Sum of Squares	Degrees of Freedom	Mean Square	Computed f
(f_1, f_3) vs (f_2, f_4)	206.67	1	206.67	17.37
f_1 vs f_3	11.48	1	11.48	0.96
Total	71.41	6	11.90	

f = 17.37 is significant at the 0.01 level; f = 0.96 is not significant.

5. H_0: $\beta_1 = \beta_2 = \beta_3 = 0$. (brand effects are zero)
H_1: At least one of the β_j's is not zero.
$\alpha = 0.05$.
Critical region: f > 3.84;
Now, from the computer printout we have

Source of Variation	Sum of Squares	Degrees of Freedom	Mean Square	Computed f
Blocks	16.54	4	4.135	
Treatments	27.80	2	13.900	5.99
Error	18.55	8	2.319	
Total	62.89	14		

P = 0.0257 Decision: Reject H_0; mean percent of foreign additives is not the same for all three brands of jam.

	Percent
Jam A	2.36
Jam B	3.48
Jam C	5.64

Based on the means, jam A appears to have the smallest amount of foreign additives.

7. H_0: $\beta_1 = \beta_2 = \cdots = \beta_6 = 0$. (station effects are zero)
H_1: At least one of the β_j's is not zero.
$\alpha = 0.01$
Critical region: f > 3.85;

Source of Variation	Sum of Squares	Degrees of Freedom	Mean Square	Computed f
Dates	3.2594	5	0.6519	
Stations	230.1271	5	46.0254	26.14
Error	44.0184	25	1.7607	
Total	277.4049	35		

P < 0.0001 Decision: Reject H_0; the mean concentration is different at the different stations.

9. H_0: $\alpha_1 = \alpha_2 = \alpha_3 = 0$. (diet effects are zero)
H_1: At least one of the α_i's is not zero.
$\alpha = 0.01$.
Critical region: $f_1 > 7.56$ with $v_1 = 2$ and $v_2 = 10$ degrees of freedom.
Computations: From the computer printout we have

Source of Variation	Sum of Squares	Degrees of Freedom	Mean Square	Computed f
Dates	4297.0000	2	2148.5000	11.86
Subjects	6033.3333	5	1206.6667	
Error	1811.6667	10	181.1667	
Total	12142.0000	17		

$P = 0.0023$ Decision: Reject H_0: differences among the diets are significant.

11. H_0: $\alpha_1 = \alpha_2 = \alpha_3 = \alpha_4 = \alpha_5 = 0$. (treatment effects are zero)
H_1: At least one of the α_i's is not zero.
$\alpha = 0.01$.
Critical region: $f_1 > 4.43$ with $v_1 = 4$ and $v_2 = 20$ degrees of freedom.
Computations: From the computer printout we have.

Source of Variation	Sum of Squares	Degrees of Freedom	Mean Square	Computed f
Treatments	79630.1333	4	19907.5333	0.58
Locations	634334.6667	5	126866.9333	
Error	689106.6667	20	34455.3333	
Total	1403071.4667	29		

$P = 0.7116$ Decision: The treatment means do not differ significantly.

13. $$\sum_i \sum_j \sum_k (y_{ijk} - \bar{y}_{...})^2 = \sum_i \sum_j \sum_k [(\bar{y}_{i..} - \bar{y}_{...}) + (\bar{y}_{.j.} - \bar{y}_{...}) + (\bar{y}_{..k} - y_{...})$$

$$+ (y_{ijk} - \bar{y}_{i..} - \bar{y}_{.j.} - \bar{y}_{..k} + 2\bar{y}_{...})]^2 = r\sum_i (\bar{y}_{i..} - \bar{y}_{...})^2 + r\sum_j (\bar{y}_{.j.} - \bar{y}_{...})^2$$

$$+ r\sum_k (\bar{y}_{..k} - \bar{y}_{...})^2 + \sum_i \sum_j \sum_k (y_{ijk} - \bar{y}_{i..} - y_{..k} + 2\bar{y}_{...})^2 + 6 \text{ cross} - \text{product terms.}$$

All cross-product terms are equal to zero.

15. H_0: $\tau_A = \tau_B = \tau_C = \tau_D = 0$. (professor effects are zero)
    H_1: At least one of the τ_K's is not zero.
    $\alpha = 0.05$

Source of Variation	Sum of Squares	Degrees of Freedom	Mean Square	Computed f
Time periods	474.5	3	158.167	
Courses	252.5	3	84.167	
Professors	723.5	3	241.167	5.03
Error	287.5	6	47.967	
Total	1738.0	15		

$P = 0.0446$ Decision: Reject H_0; Grades are affected by different professors.

17.
```
    Source of                 Sum of        Mean
    Variation    DF          Squares        Square    F-value    P-Value
    PLANT         1          53.7004       53.7004
    AMOUNT        2        1238.8825      619.4412     122.37     <0.0001
    Error        20         101.2433        5.0622
    Total        23        1393.8262

Duncan Groupings
  Temperature       3%          1%          .3%
  Mean          23.375      12.750       5.912
```

Mean color density is significantly better with 3% dye and 1% is better than .33%.

Section 13.14 Case Study

1.   From the computer printout we have

Source of Variation	Sum of Squares	Degrees of Freedom	Mean Square	Computed f
Operators	371.8719	3	123.9573	14.9
Error	99.7925	12	8.3160	
Total	471.6644	15		

$P = 0.0002$ Decision: Reject H_0; operators are different.

$\hat{\sigma}_u^2 = (123.96 - 8.32)/4 = 28.91$; $\hat{\sigma}^2 = 8.32$.

79

3.   (a) H_0: $\alpha_1 = \alpha_2 = \alpha_3 = \alpha_4 = 0$. (treatment effects are zero)

           H_1: At least one of the α_i's is not zero.

           $\alpha = 0.05$.

           Critical region: $f_1 > 3.49$ with $v_1 = 3$ and $v_2 = 12$ degrees of freedom.

           Computations: From the computer printout we have

Source of Variation	Sum of Squares	Degrees of Freedom	Mean Square	Computed f
Treatments	23.24	3	7.75	3.33
Blocks	45.28	4	11.32	
Error	27.94	12	2.33	
Total	96.46	19		

           $P = 0.0564$ Decision: Not able to show a significant difference in treatments at the .05 level of significance.

    (b) $\hat{\sigma}_\alpha^2 = (7.75 - 2.33)/5 = 1.08$; $\hat{\sigma}_\beta^2 = (11.32 - 2.33)/4 = 2.25$.

5.   (a)

$$A = \begin{bmatrix} bk & b & b & \cdots & b & k & k & \cdots & k \\ b & b & 0 & \cdots & 0 & 1 & 1 & \cdots & 1 \\ b & 0 & b & \cdots & 0 & 1 & 1 & \cdots & 1 \\ \cdot & \cdot & \cdot & \cdot & \cdot & \cdot & \cdot & & \cdot \\ \cdot & \cdot & \cdot & & \cdot & \cdot & \cdot & & \cdot \\ \cdot & \cdot & \cdot & & \cdot & \cdot & \cdot & & \cdot \\ b & 0 & 0 & \cdots & b & 1 & 1 & \cdots & 1 \\ k & 1 & 1 & \cdots & 1 & k & 0 & \cdots & 0 \\ k & 1 & 1 & \cdots & 1 & 0 & k & \cdots & 0 \\ \cdot & \cdot & \cdot & & \cdot & \cdot & \cdot & & \cdot \\ \cdot & \cdot & \cdot & & \cdot & \cdot & \cdot & & \cdot \\ \cdot & \cdot & \cdot & & \cdot & \cdot & \cdot & & \cdot \\ k & 1 & 1 & \cdots & 1 & 0 & 0 & \cdots & k \end{bmatrix}$$

where b = number of blocks and k = number of treatments.

$$\underline{B} = \begin{bmatrix} \mu \\ \alpha_1 \\ \alpha_2 \\ \cdot \\ \cdot \\ \cdot \\ \alpha_k \\ \beta_1 \\ \beta_2 \\ \cdot \\ \cdot \\ \cdot \\ \beta_b \end{bmatrix} \qquad \mathbf{g} = \begin{bmatrix} T_{..} \\ T_{1.} \\ T_{2.} \\ \cdot \\ \cdot \\ \cdot \\ T_{k.} \\ T_{.1} \\ T_{.2} \\ \cdot \\ \cdot \\ \cdot \\ T_{.b} \end{bmatrix}$$

(b) Solving the system $\underline{A}\underline{b} = \mathbf{g}$ with the constraints $\sum_{i=1}^{k}\alpha_i = 0$, $\sum_{j=1}^{b}\beta_j = 0$, we have

$$\hat{\mu} = \bar{y}_{..}$$
$$\hat{\alpha}_i = \bar{y}_{i.} - \bar{y}_{..}, \ (i = 1, 2, ..., k)$$
$$\hat{\beta}_j = \bar{y}_{.j} - \bar{y}_{..}, \ (j = 1, 2, ..., b).$$

Therefore,

$$R(\alpha_1, \alpha_2, ..., \alpha_k, \beta_1, \beta_2, ..., \beta_b) = \underline{b}'\mathbf{g} - (T_{..})^2/bk$$
$$= \sum_{i=1}^{k} T_{i.}^2/b + \sum_{j=1}^{b} T_j^2/k - 2(T_{..})^2/bk .$$

To find $R(\beta_1, \beta_2, ..., \beta_b \mid \alpha_1, \alpha_2, ..., \alpha_k)$ we first find $R(\alpha_1, \alpha_2, ..., \alpha_k)$. Setting $\beta_j = 0$ in the model, we obtain as estimates (after applying the constraint $\sum_{i=1}^{k}\alpha_i = 0$)

$$\hat{\mu} = \bar{y}_{..}$$
and
$$\hat{\alpha}_i = \bar{y}_{i.} - \bar{y}_{..}, \ i = 1, 2, ..., k.$$

The $\mathbf{g}$ vector is the same as in part (a) with the exception that $T_{.1}, T_{.2}, ..., T_{.b}$ do not appear. Thus one obtains

$$R(\alpha_1, \alpha_2, ..., \alpha_k) = \sum_{i=1}^{k} T_{i.}^2/b - T_{..}^2/bk$$
and thus

$$R(\beta_1, \beta_2, ..., \beta_b \mid \alpha_1, \alpha_2, ..., \alpha_k) = R(\alpha_1, \alpha_2, ..., \alpha_k, \beta_1, \beta_2, ..., \beta_b) - R(\alpha_1 \alpha_2, ..., \alpha_k)$$
$$= \sum_{j=1}^{b} T_j^2/k - T_{..}^2/bk = SSB.$$

7. $$\phi^2 = b\sum_{i=1}^{4} \alpha_i^2 / 4\sigma^2 = b/2, \text{ when } \sum_{i=1}^{4} \alpha_i^2 / \sigma^2 = 2.0.$$

If $b = 10$, $\phi = 2.24$; $v_1 = 3$ and $v_2 = 27$ degrees of freedom.
If $b = 9$, $\phi = 2.12$; $v_1 = 3$ and $v_2 = 24$ degrees of freedom.
If $b = 8$, $\phi = 2.00$; $v_1 = 3$ and $v_2 = 21$ degrees of freedom.

From Table A.15 we see that $b = 9$ gives the desired result.

9. (a) $y_{ij} = \mu + \alpha_i + \varepsilon_{ij}$; $\alpha_1 \sim N(0, \sigma_\alpha^2)$.

(b) $\hat{\sigma}^2 = 0.0206$; $\hat{\sigma}_\alpha^2 = 0.00$ since

$$\hat{\sigma}_\alpha^2 = \frac{\sigma^2 - \sigma_\alpha^2}{10} = \frac{0.0179 - 0.0206}{10} = -0.00027.$$

11. (a) $y_{ij} = \mu + \alpha_i + \varepsilon_{ij}$; $\alpha_1 \sim N(0, \sigma_\alpha^2)$.

(b) $f = 5.63$; $P[F > 5.63] = 0.0121$;
Yes, the loom variance component is significantly different from 0.

(c) The suspicion is supported by the data.

Chapter 14
Factorial Experiments (Two or More Factors)

Section 14.4 Graphical Analysis in the Two-Factor Problem

1. (a) H_0': $\alpha_1 = \alpha_2 = \alpha_3 = 0$.

    H_1': At least one of the α_i's is not zero.

    (b) H_0'': $\beta_1 = \beta_2 = \beta_3 = \beta_4 = 0$.

    H_1'': At least one of the β_i's is not zero.

    (c) H_0''': $(\alpha\beta)_{11} = (\alpha\beta)_{12} = \cdots = (\alpha\beta)_{34} = 0$.

    H_1''': At least one of the $(\alpha\beta)_{ij}$'s is not zero.

$\alpha = 0.05$.

Critical region: (a) $f_1 > 3.00$; (b) $f_2 > 3.89$; (c) $f_3 > 3.49$.

Computations: From the computer printout we have

Source of Variation	Sum of Squares	Degrees of Freedom	Mean Square	Computed f
Temperatures	5194.08	2	2597.0400	8.12
Ovens	4963.12	3	1654.3733	5.18
Interaction	3126.26	6	521.0433	1.63
Error	3833.50	12	319.4583	
Total	17,116.96	23		

Decisions: (a) Reject H_0';   (b) Reject H_0'';   (c) Do not reject H_0'''

3. (a) H_0': $\alpha_1 = \alpha_2 = 0$. (no differences in the environments)

    H_1': The α_i's are not zero.

    (b) H_0'': $\beta_1 = \beta_2 = \beta_3 = 0$. (no differences in the strains)

    H_1'': At least one of the β_j's is not zero.

    (c) H_0''': $(\alpha\beta)_{11} = (\alpha\beta)_{12} = \cdots = (\alpha\beta)_{23} = 0$. (environments and strains do not interact)

    H_1''': At least one of the $(\alpha\beta)_{ij}$'s is not equal to zero.

$\alpha = 0.01$

Critical regions: (a) $f_1 > 7.29$; (b) $f_2 > 5.16$; (c) $f_3 > 5.16$.

Computations: From the printout we have

Source of Variation	Sum of Squares	Degrees of Freedom	Mean Square	Computed f
Environments	14,875	1	14,875	14.81
Strains	18,154	2	9,077	9.04
Interaction	1,235	2	617.5	0.61
Error	42,193	42	1,004.6	
Total	76,457	47		

Decisions: Reject H_0' and H_0''; do not reject H_0'''. That is, environments and strains affect the scores. There is no significant interaction.

5. (a) H_0': $\alpha_1 = \alpha_2 = \alpha_3 = 0$.

   H_1': At least one of the α_i's is not zero.

   (b) H_0'': $\beta_1 = \beta_2 = \beta_3 = \beta_4 = \beta_5 = 0$.

   H_1'': At least one of the β_j's is not zero.

   (c) H_0''': $(\alpha\beta)_{11} = (\alpha\beta)_{12} = \cdots = (\alpha\beta)_{35} = 0$.

   H_1''': At least one of the $(\alpha\beta)_{ij}$'s is not zero.

$\alpha = 0.01$.
Critical regions: (a) $f_1 < 5.39$; (b) $f_2 > 4.02$; (c) $f_3 > 3.17$.

Source of Variation	Sum of Squares	Degrees of Freedom	Mean Square	Computed f
Subjects	4814.7444	2	2407.3722	34.40
Muscles	7543.8667	4	1885.9667	26.95
Interaction	11362.2000	8	1420.2750	20.30
Error	2099.1667	30	69.9722	
Total	25819.9778	44		

Decisions: (a) Reject H_0'; (b) Reject H_0''; (c) Reject H_0'''.

7.

Source of Variation	df	Sum of Squares	Mean Square	F-value	P-Value
Amount	4	2466.6500	616.6625000	46.63	0.0001
Temp	3	430.4750	143.4916667	10.85	0.0002
Amount*Temp	12	326.1500	27.1791667	2.06	0.0745
Error	20	264.5000	13.2250000		
Total	39	3487.7750			

Duncan Grouping	Mean	N	TEMP
A	60.300	10	60
A			
A	59.800	10	70
A	59.000	10	80
B	52.200	10	50

Duncan Grouping	Mean	N	AMOUNT
A	66.250	8	0.8
A			
A	64.625	8	0.7
B	58.125	8	0.9
B			
B	56.000	8	0.6
C	44.125	8	0.5

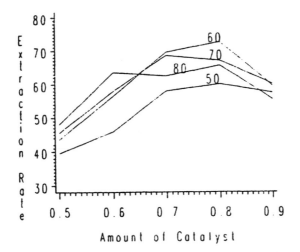

9.   (a)

Source	DF	Anova SS	Mean Square	F Value	Pr > F
tool	1	675.0000000	675.0000000	74.31	<.0001
speed	1	12.0000000	12.0000000	1.32	0.2836
tool*speed	1	192.0000000	192.0000000	21.14	0.0018
Error	8	72.6666667	9.0833333		

(b)   The cutting speed that results in the longest life of the machine tool depends on the tool geometry. Variability is much greater with tool geometry at level one.

(c)   For tool geometry = 1 an f-test on cutting speed yields an f = (150.00/1)/9.0833 = 16.51; P-value = 0.0036.
Speed = High, mean = 33.333; Speed = Low, mean = 23.333;
A high cutting speed produces a significantly longer life for tool geometry at level one.
For tool geometry = 2 an f-test on cutting speed yields an f = (54.00/1)9.0833 = 5.94; P-value = 0.0407.
Speed = High, mean = 10.333; Speed = Low, mean = 16.333;
A low cutting speed produces a significantly longer life for tool geometry at level one.

(d)

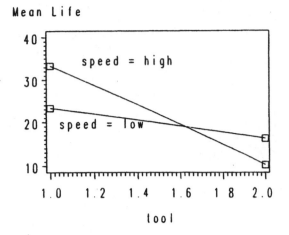

Section 14.5 Three Factor Experiments

1.　　From the computer printout we have

Source of Variation	Sum of Squares	Degrees of Freedom	Mean Square	Computed f
Main Effect				
A	2.24073	1	2.24073	0.54
B	56.31814	2	28.15907	6.85
C	17.65148	2	8.82574	2.15
Two-factor interaction				
AB	31.47146	2	15.73573	3.83
AC	31.20257	2	15.601285	3.79
BC	21.56072	4	5.39018	1.31
Three-factor interaction				
ABC	26.79849	4	6.699623	1.63
Error	148.03969	36	4.1122136	
Total	76,457	53		

(a)　Since $f_{0.05}(2, 36) \cong 3.27$ and $f_{0.05}(4, 36) \cong 2.64$, only the AB and AC interactions are significant.

(b)　Since $f_{0.05}(1, 36) \cong 4.12$ and $f_{0.05}(2, 36) \cong 2.64$, only factor B is significant.

(c)　At level A_1, the effect of C is to reduce the response in going from C_1 to C_2, whereas at level A_1, this is not the case. As a result, the totals in response for C_1, C_2, C_3 do not deviate a great deal, the AC interaction having masked the effect of C. The overall test on factor C is misleading here.

3. Letting A, B, and C designate coating, humidity, and stress, respectively, the computer printout yields the following results:

Source of Variation	Sum of Squares	Degrees of Freedom	Mean Square	Computed f
Main Effect				
A	216,384	1	216,384	0.05
B	19,876,891	2	9,938,446	2.13
C	427,993,946	2	213,996,973	45.96
Two-factor interaction				
AB	31,736,626	2	15,868,313	3.41
AC	699,830	2	349,915	0.08
BC	58,623,693	4	14,655,923	3.15
Three-factor interaction				
ABC	36,034,809	4	9,008,702	1.93
Error	335,213,134	72	4,655,738	
Total	910,395,313	89		

(a) Level of stress (C) with $f_{2, 72} = 45.96$ and a P-value < 0.0001 is significant at the $\alpha = 0.01$ level. The coating (A) by humidity (B) interaction has a P-value of 0.0385 and the stress times humidity interaction has a P-value of 0.0192. Both of these interactions are significant at the $\alpha = 0.05$ level.

(b) A stress level of 20 consistently produces low fatigue. It appears to work best with medium humidity and an uncoated surface.

5.

Source of Variation	DF	Sum of Squares	Mean Square	F-value	P-value
TEMP	2	0.1662	0.0831	14.22	0.0001
SURFACE	2	0.0782	0.0391	6.70	0.0020
HRC	2	0.0195	0.0097	1.67	0.1954
TEMP*SURFACE	4	0.1284	0.0321	5.50	0.0006
TEMP*HRC	4	0.0628	0.0157	2.69	0.0369
SURFACE*HRC	4	0.1264	0.0316	5.41	0.0007
TEMP*SURFACE*HR	8	0.1412	0.0176	3.02	0.0051
Error	81	0.4732	0.0058		
Total	107	1.1960			

There is a significant temperature by surface by hrc interaction.
A plot for each temperature is given to illustrate the interaction.

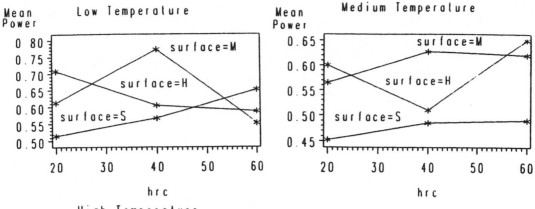

7. (a) Yes. brand* type, $f_{2,24} = (200.7222/2)7.1667 = 14.00$; P-value < 0.0001.
        brand*temp, $f_{2,24} = (187.0556/2)/7.1667 = 13.05$; P-value = <0.0001.

    (b) The three brands averaged across the other two factors are significantly different from one another. $f_{2,24} = (833.7222/2)7.1667 = 58.17$; P-value < 0.0001.

    (c) Using brand Y, powdered detergent and hot water yields the highest percent removal of dirt.

Section 14.7 Choice of Sample Size

1. (a) H_0: $\sigma^2_{\alpha\beta} = 0$.

        H_1: $\sigma^2_{\alpha\beta} \neq 0$.

        $\alpha = 0.05$.
        Critical region f > 2.51; $f_{6,24} = (1.65722/6)/4.44005 = 1.49$; P-value = 0.2238.
        The null hypothesis cannot be rejected. There is no significant interaction variance component.

(b) H_0': $\sigma_\alpha^2 = 0$ H_0'': $\sigma_\beta^2 = 0$

H_α': $\sigma_\alpha^2 \neq 0$ H_α'': $\sigma_\beta^2 \neq 0$

$\alpha = 0.05$.

Critical regions: $f_1 > 5.14$; $f_2 > 4.76$.

Computations: From the computer printout we have SSA = 4.63386, SSB = 10.31776 and SS(AB) = 1.65722 with 2, 3, and 6 degrees of freedom, respectively. Therefore,

$$f_1 = \frac{4.63386/2}{1.65722/6} = 8.39 \text{ (filters),}$$

and

$$f_2 = \frac{10.31776/3}{1.65722/6} = 12.45 \quad \text{(operators).}$$

Decisions: Reject H_0' and H_0''; both σ_α^2 and σ_β^2 are significant.

(c) $\hat{\sigma}_\alpha^2 = [(4.63386/2) - (1.65722/6)]/12 = 0.1701$ (filters)

$\hat{\sigma}_\beta^2 = [(10.31776/3) - (1.65722/6)]/9 = 0.3514$ (operators),

$s^2 = 4.44005/24 = 0.1867$.

3.

Source of Variation	Degrees of Freedom	Mean Square	(a) Computed f	(b) Computed f
A	3	$s_1^2 = 140$	$s_1^2/s_5^2 = 5.83$	$s_1^2/s_5^2 = 5.83$
B	1	$s_2^2 = 480$	$s_2^2/s_{p_3}^2 = 78.82$	$s_2^2/s_6^2 = 26.67$
C	2	$s_3^2 = 325$	$s_3^2/s_5^2 = 13.54$	$s_3^2/s_5^2 = 13.54$
AB	3	$s_4^2 = 15$	$s_4^2/s_{p_2}^2 = 2.86$	$s_4^2/s_7^2 = 7.50$
AC	6	$s_5^2 = 24$	$s_5^2/s_{p_2}^2 = 4.57$	$s_5^2/s_7^2 = 12.00$
BC	2	$s_6^2 = 18$	$s_6^2/s_{p_1}^2 = 4.09$	$s_6^2/s_7^2 = 9.00$
ABC	6	$s_7^2 = 2$	$s_7^2/s^2 = 0.40$	$s_7^2/s^2 = 0.40$
Error	24	$s^2 = 5$		
Total	47			

In column (a) we have found the following main effects and interaction effect significant using the pooled estimates.

$$\hat{\sigma}_\beta^2, \hat{\sigma}_\gamma^2, \hat{\sigma}_{\alpha\gamma}^2$$

$s_{p_1}^2 = (12 + 120)/30 = 4.4$ with 30 degrees of freedom.

$s_{p_2}^2 = (12 + 120 + 36)/32 = 5.25$ with 32 degrees of freedom.

$s_{p_3}^2 = (12 + 120 + 36 + 45)/35 = 6.09$ with 35 degrees of freedom.

In column (b) we have found $\hat{\sigma}_\gamma^2$ and $\hat{\sigma}_{\alpha\gamma}^2$ significant when sums of squares of insignificant effects were not pooled.

5. $1 - \beta = P[F(2, 6) > f_{0.05}(2, 6)(\sigma^2 + 3\sigma^2_{\alpha\beta})/(\sigma^2 + 3\sigma^2_{\alpha\beta} + 12\sigma^2_{\beta})]$

$\quad = P[F(2, 6) > (5.14)(0.2762)/2.3169]$

$\quad = P[F(2, 6) > 0.6127].$

From Table A-7c of <u>Introduction to Statistical Analysis</u> by Dixon and Massey we find

$\quad 1 - \beta = 0.59.$

7. (a) A mixed model.

(b)

Source	df	ss	ms	f	p
brand	2	0.6065	0.3033	1.73	0.2875
material	2	1.0349	0.5174	47.42	<0.0001
b*m	4	0.7011	0.1753	16.06	0.0004
error	9	0.0982	0.0109		
total	17	2.4407			

(c) No. Brand A has the highest estimated mean, but it was not significantly higher than brands B and C. More materials, thus more error degrees-of-freedom might help to prove the claim.

9, (a) A mixed model. Cereal type β_j in the model) is a random effect.
Power setting (α_i in the model) is a fixed effect.

$y_{ijk} = \mu + \alpha_i + \beta_j + \alpha\beta_{ij} + \varepsilon_{ijk};$

$\sum \alpha_i = 0; \; \beta_j \sim N(0, \sigma^2_{\beta}), \; (\alpha\beta)_{ij} \sim N(0, \sigma^2_{\alpha\beta}), \; \varepsilon_{ijk} \sim N(0, \sigma^2);$

(b) No. $f_{2,4} = 1.37; \; P[F > 1.37] = 0.3524.$

(c) No. The estimate of σ^2_{β} is negative.

Chapter 15
2^k Factorial Experiments and Fractions

Section 15.4 Injection Molding Case Study

1.   From Table 15.3 of the text

$$\begin{aligned}
\text{SSA} &= (-41 + 51 - 57 - 63 + 67 + 54 - 76 + 73)^2/24 \\
&= 2.6667, \\
\text{SSB} &= (-41 - 51 + 57 - 63 + 67 - 54 + 76 + 73)^2/24 \\
&= 170.6667, \\
\text{SSC} &= (-41 - 51 - 57 + 63 - 67 + 54 + 76 + 73)^2/24 \\
&= 104.1667, \\
\text{SS(AB)} &= (41 - 51 - 57 + 63 + 67 - 54 - 76 + 73)^2/24 \\
&= 1.5000, \\
\text{SS(AC)} &= (41 - 51 + 57 - 63 - 67 + 54 - 76 + 73)^2/24 \\
&= 42.6667, \\
\text{SS(BC)} &= (41 + 51 - 57 - 63 - 67 - 54 + 76 + 73)^2/24 \\
&= 0.0000, \\
\text{SS(ABC)} &= (-41 + 51 + 57 + 63 - 67 - 54 - 76 + 73)^2/24 \\
&= 1.5000.
\end{aligned}$$

3.   From the computer printout the following results are obtained:

Source	DF	Anova SS	F-value	P-value
A	1	11.52000000	4.68	0.0459
B	1	12.00500000	4.88	0.0421
A*B	1	7.80125000	3.17	0.0939
C	1	39.60500000	16.10	0.0010
A*C	1	3.0012500	1.22	0.2857
B*C	1	11.28125000	4.59	0.0480
A*B*C	1	2.42000000	0.98	0.3360
D	1	17.70125000	7.20	0.0163
A*D	1	14.04500000	5.71	0.0295
B*D	1	3.12500000	1.27	0.2763
A*B*D	1	24.15125000	9.82	0.0064
C*D	1	3.92000000	1.59	0.2249
A*C*D	1	17.70125000	7.20	0.0163
B*C*D	1	5.95125000	2.42	0.1394
A*B*C*D	1	3.92000000	1.59	0.2249
Error	16	39.36000000		
Total	31	217.50875000		

The A*D and the B*C interaction plots are printed below. The A*D plot varies with levels of C since the A*C*D interaction is significant or levels of B since the A*B*D interaction is significant.

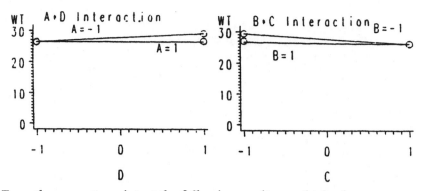

5. From the computer printout the following results are obtained:

Source	DF	Anova SS	F-value	P-value
STATE	1	0.00062500	0.02	0.8863
TIME	1	0.27562500	9.98	0.0251
SPEED	1	0.00562500	0.20	0.6707
COND	1	0.18062500	6.54	0.0508
STATE*TIME	1	0.01562500	0.57	0.4859
STATE*SPEED	1	0.05062500	1.83	0.2338
STATE*COND	1	0.00062500	0.02	0.8863
TIME*SPEED	1	0.05062500	1.83	0.2338
TIME*COND	1	0.00562500	0.20	0.6707
SPEED*COND	1	0.52562500	19.03	0.0073
Error	5	0.13812500		
Total	10	1.24937500		

Mixing time and nitrogen condition are significant.
Blade speed*nitrogen condition is significant.

Section 15.6 Partial Confounding

1.

Block	
1	2
(1)	a
c	b
ab	ac
abc	bc

Rep. 1
AB confounded

Block	
1	2
(1)	a
c	b
ab	ac
abc	bc

Rep. 2
AB confounded

Block	
1	2
(1)	a
c	b
ab	ac
abc	bc

Rep. 3
AB confounded

Analysis of Variance

Source of Variation	Degrees of Freedom
Blocks	5
A	1
B	1
C	1
AC	1
BC	1
ABC	1
Error	12
Total	23

3. $L_1 = \gamma_1 + \gamma_2 + \gamma_3, \qquad L_2 = \gamma_1 + \gamma_2 + \gamma_4.$

For treatment combination (1) we find L_1 (mod 2) = 0 and L_2 (mod 2) = 0. For treatment combination $\underline{a}$ we find L_1 (mod 2) = 1 and L_2 (mod 2) = 1. After evaluating L_1 and L_2 for all sixteen treatment combinations we obtain the following blocking scheme:

Block 1	Block 2	Block 3	Block 4
(1)	c	d	a
ab	abc	ac	b
acd	ad	bc	cd
bcd	bd	abd	abcd
$L_1 = 0$	$L_1 = 1$	$L_1 = 0$	$L_1 = 1$
$L_2 = 0$	$L_2 = 0$	$L_2 = 1$	$L_2 = 1$

Since $(ABC)(ABD) = A^2B^2CD = CD(\text{mod } 2)$, then CD is the other effect confounded.

5. $L = \gamma_1 + \gamma_2 + \gamma_3, \qquad L_2 = \gamma_1 + \gamma_2.$

For treatment combination (1) we find $L_1(\text{mod } 2) = 0$ and $L_2(\text{mod } 2) = 0$. For treatment combination $\underline{a}$ we find $L_1(\text{mod } 2) = 1$ and $L(\text{mod } 2) = 1$. Rep. 1 and Rep. 2 have $L_1 = 0$ in one block and $L_1 = 1$ in the other. Rep. 3 has $L_2 = 0$ in one block and $L_2 = 0$ in the other.

Block	
1	2
abc	ab
a	ac
b	bc
c	(1)

Rep. 1
AB confounded

Block	
1	2
abc	ab
a	ac
b	bc
c	(1)

Rep. 2
AB confounded

Block	
1	2
(1)	a
c	b
ab	ac
abc	bc

Rep. 3
AB confounded

Analysis of Variance

Source of Variation	Degrees of Freedom
Blocks	5
A	1
B	1
C	1
AB	1′
AC	1
BC	1
ABC	1′
Error	11
Total	23

Relative Information on ABC = 1/3.

Relative information on AB = 2/3.

7.   (a)   One possible design would be:

Machine

1	2	3	4
(1)	a	c	d
ab	b	abc	abd
ce	ace	e	cde
abce	bce	abe	abcde
acd	cd	ad	ac
bde	abde	bcde	be
ade	de	acde	ae
bcd	abcd	bd	bc

(b)   ABD, CDE, ABCE

Section 15.10   Analysis of Fractional Factorial Experiments

1.   The alias for each effect is obtained by multiplying each effect by the defining contrast and reducing the exponents modulo 2.

$A \equiv CDE$	$AB \equiv BCDE$	$BD \equiv ABCE$
$B \equiv ABCDE$	$AC \equiv DE$	$BE \equiv ABCD$
$C \equiv ADE$	$AD \equiv CE$	$ABC \equiv BDE$
$D \equiv ACE$	$AE \equiv CD$	$ABD \equiv BCE$
$E \equiv ACD$	$BC \equiv ABDE$	$ABE \equiv BCD$

3.   With ABCD and BDEF as defining contrasts, we have

$$L = = \gamma_1 + \gamma_2 + \gamma_3 + \gamma_4, \ L_2 = \gamma_2 + \gamma_4 + \gamma_5 + \gamma_6.$$

The following treatment combinations give $L_1 = 0$, $L_2 = 0$ (modulo 2) and thereby suffice as the 1/4 fraction:

$\{(1), ac, bd, abcd, abe, bce, ade, cde, abf, bcf, adf, cdf, ef, acef, bdef, abcdef\}$.

The third defining contrast is given by

$$(ABCD)(BDEF) = AB^2CD^2EF$$
$$= ACEF \text{ (modulo 2)}.$$

The effects that are aliased with the six main effects are:

$$A \equiv BCD \equiv ABDEF \equiv CEF$$
$$B \equiv ACD \equiv DEF \equiv ABCEF$$
$$C \equiv ABD \equiv BCDEF \equiv AEF$$
$$D \equiv ABC \equiv BEF \equiv ACDEF$$
$$E \equiv ABCDE \equiv BDF \equiv ACF$$
$$F \equiv ABCDF \equiv BDE \equiv ACE$$

5. Using the contrast method to compute sums of squares, we have

Source of Variation	Sum of Squares	Degrees of Freedom	Mean Square	Computed f
A	1.44	1	1.44	0.48
B	4.00	1	4.00	1.35
C	9.00	1	9.00	3.03
D	5.76	1	5.76	1.94
E	16.00	1	16.00	5.39
F	3.24	1	3.24	1.09
G	12.96	1	12.96	4.36
Error	23.76	8	2.97	
Total		15		

The error term is computed by pooling all the interaction effects. Factor E is the only significant effect.

7. Two-factor interactions are aliased with each other.
The two-factor interactions with the largest mean squares were tested and others were included in the error term.

Source of Variation	DF	Sum of Squares	Mean Square	F-Value	P-Value
A	1	81.5409	81.5409	0.29	0.6044
B	1	166.5390	166.5390	0.60	0.4636
C	1	5.6406	5.6406	0.02	0.8906
D	1	4.4100	4.4100	0.02	0.9032
E	1	40.1956	40.1956	0.15	0.7146
F	1	678.5409	1678.5409	6.06	0.0434
A*C	1	978.7512	978.7512	3.53	0.1023
B*D	1	429.5256	429.5256	1.55	0.2532
Error	7	940.0902	277.1557		
Total	15	5325.2341			

F, the location of detection, appears to be the only significant main effect. The A*C interaction has the next smallest P-value. A*C is aliased with B*E.

Section 15.14 Taguchi's Robust Parameter Design

1. $\hat{y} = 12.7519 + 4.7194x_1 + 0.8656x_2 - 1.4156x_3$
       Units are centered and scaled. Lack of fit:

       $F = 81.58$ $P < 0.0001$

3.   AFG CEFG ACDF BEG BDFG ABEF CDG BCDE ABCDEFG DEF ADEG

Chapter 16
Nonparametric Statistics

Section 16.3 Signed-Rank Test

1. H_0: $\mu = 20$ minutes
    H_1: $\mu > 20$ minutes
    $\alpha = 0.05$
    Test Statistic: Binomial variable X with $p = 1/2$.
    Computations: Subtracting 20 from each observation and discarding the zero's, we obtain the signs

    $$- \; + \; + \; - \; + \; + \; - \; + \; + \; +$$

    for which $n = 10$ and $x = 7$. Therefore, the P value is

    $$P = P(X \geq 7 \text{ when } p = 1/2)$$
    $$= \sum_{x=7}^{10} b(x; 10, 1/2) = 1 - \sum_{x=0}^{6} b(x; 10, 1/2)$$
    $$= 1 - 0.0821 = 0.1719 > 0.05.$$

    Decision: Do not reject H_0.

3. H_0: $\mu = 2.5$
    H_1: $\mu \neq 2.5$.
    $\alpha = 0.05$.
    Test statistic: Binomial variable X with $p = 1/2$.
    Computations: We obtain the sequence.

    $$- \; - \; - \; - \; - \; - \; - \; + \; + \; - \; + \; - \; - \; - \; - \; -$$

    for which $n = 16$ and $x = 3$. Therefore, $\mu = np = (16)(0.5) = 8$ and $\sigma = \sqrt{npq} = \sqrt{(16)(0.5)(0.5)} = 2$. Hence, $z = (3.5 - 8)/2 = -2.25$, and then

    $$P = 2P(X \leq 3) \cong 2P(Z < -2.25)$$
    $$= (2)(0.0122) = 0.0244 < 0.05.$$

    Decision: Reject H_0.

5. H_0: $\mu_1 - \mu_2 = 45$
    H_1: $\mu_1 - \mu_2 < 45$
    $\alpha = 0.05$.
    Test statistic: Binomial variable X with $p = 1/2$.
    Computations: We have $n = 10$ and $x = 4$ plus signs. Therefore, the P-value is

    $$P = P(X < 4 \text{ when } p = 1/2) = \sum_{x=0}^{4} b(x; 10, 1/2)$$
    $$= 0.3770 > 0.05.$$

    Decision: Do not reject H_0.

7. H_0: $\mu_2 - \mu_1 = 8$
    H_1: $\mu_2 - \mu_1 = 8$
    $\alpha = 0.05$.
    Test Statistic: Binomial variable X with p = 1/2.
    Computations: We have n = 13 and x = 4. Therefore, $\mu = np = (13)(1/2) = 6.5$ and
    $\sigma = \sqrt{npq} = \sqrt{(13)(1/2)(1/2)} = \sqrt{13}/2$.
    Hence, $z = (4.5 - 6.5)/(\sqrt{12}/2) = -1.11$, and then
    $$P = P(X \le 4) = P(Z < -1.11)$$
    $$= 0.1355 > 0.05.$$

9. H_0: $\mu = 12$
    H_1: $\mu \ne 12$
    $\alpha = 0.02$
    Critical region: $w \le 20$ for n = 15.
    Computations:

d_i	−3	1	−2	−1	6	4	1	2	−1	3	−3	1	2	−1	2
Rank	12	3.5	8.5	3.5	15	14	3.5	8.5	3.5	12	12	3.5	8.5	3.5	8.5

    Now, $w_- = 43$ and $W_+ = 77$, so that $w = 43$.
    Decision: Do not reject H_0:

11. H_0: $\mu_1 - \mu_2 = 4.5$
    H_1: $\mu_1 - \mu_2 < 4.5$
    $\alpha = 0.05$
    Critical region: $w_+ \le 11$
    Computations:

Woman	1	2	3	4	5	6	7	8	9	10
d_i	−1.5	5.4	3.6	6.9	5.5	2.7	2.3	3.4	5.9	0.7
$d_i - d_0$	−6.0	0.9	−0.9	2.4	1.0	−1.8	−2.2	−1.1	1.4	−3.8
Rank	10	1.5	1.5	8	3	6	7	4	5	9

    Therefore, $w_+ = 17.5$.
    Decision: Do not reject H_0.

13. H_0: $\mu_1 - \mu_2 = 8$
    H_a: $\mu_1 - \mu_2 < 8$.
    $\alpha = 0.05$.
    Critical region: $z < -1.645$.

98

Computations:

Diff.	Adj. Diff.	Rank		Diff.	Adj. Diff.	Rank
6	–2	4.5		8	0	–
9	1	1.5		2	–6	12
3	–5	10.5		6	–2	4.5
5	–3	7.5		3	–5	10.5
8	0	–		1	–7	13
9	1	1.5		6	–2	4.5
4	–4	9		8	0	–
10	2	4.5		11	3	7.5

Discarding zero differences, we have $w_+ = 15$, $n = 13$,

$\mu_{w_+} = (13)(14)/4 = 45.5$, $\sigma_{w_+} = \sqrt{(13)(14)(27)/24} = 14.309$.

Therefore, $z = (15 - 45.5)/14.309 = -2.13$.

Decision: Reject H_0; the average increase is less than 8 points.

Section 16.5 Kruskal-Wallis Test

1. H_0: $\mu_B = \mu_A$
    H_1: $\mu_B < \mu_A$
    $\alpha = 0.05$
    Critical region: $u_1 = u_1 < 1$
    Computations:

Original data	7	8	9	10	11	12	13	14
Rank	1	2	3	4	5	6	7	8

    Now, $w_1 = 7$ and hence $u_1 = 7 - [(3)(4)/2] = 1$.

    Decision: Reject H_0; the claim is valid.

3. H_0: $\mu_A = \mu_B$
    H_1: $\mu_A > \mu_B$

Data	Rank		Data	Rank
3.8	1*		5.0	10
4.0	2*		5.1	11
4.2	3*		5.2	12*
4.3	4*		5.3	13
4.5	5.5*		5.5	14
4.5	5.5*		5.6	15
4.6	7		5.8	16
4.8	8*		6.2	17
4.9	9*		6.3	18

    *Calculator B

    $\alpha = 0.01$. Critical region = $\mu_B \leq 14$.
    Now, $w_2 = 50$ and hence $\mu_B = 50 - [(9)(10)/2] = 5$.
    Decision: Reject H_0; Calculator A operates longer.

5. H_0: $\mu_1 = \mu_2$
H_1: $\mu_1 \neq \mu_2$
$\alpha = 0.05$
Critical region: $u \leq 5$.
Computations:

Original data	64	67	69	75	78	79	80	82	87	88	91	93
Rank	1	2	3	4	5	6	7	8	9	10	11	12

Now, $w_1 = 35$ and $w_2 = 43$. Therefore
$u_1 = 35 - [(5)(6)/2] = 20$,
$u_2 = 43 - [(7)(8)/2] = 15$,
so that $u = 15$.
Decision: Do not reject H_0:

7. H_0: Operating times for all three calculators are equal.
H_1: Operating times are not all equal.
$\alpha = 0.01$

Critical region: $h > \chi^2_{0.01} = 9,210$ with $v = 2$ degrees of freedom
Computations:

A	B	C
4	8.5	15
12	7	18
1	13	10
2	11	16
6	8.5	14
$r_1 = 25$	5	17
	3	$r_3 = 90$
	$r_2 = 56$	

Now,

$$h = \frac{12}{(18)(19)} \left[\frac{25^2}{5} + \frac{56^2}{7} + \frac{90^2}{6} \right] - (3)(19) = 10.47.$$

Decision: Reject H_0; The operating times for all three calculators are not equal.

Section 16.8 Rank Correlation Coefficient

1. H_0: Sample is random
H_1: Sample is not random
$\alpha = 0.01$
Test statistic: V, the total number of runs.
Computations: For the given sequence we obtain $n_1 = 5$, $n_2 = 10$, and $v = 7$. Therefore, from Table A.18, the P value is
$P = 2P(V \leq 7$ when H_0 is true)
$= (2)(0.455) = 0.910 > 0.1$.

Decision: Do not reject H_0 ; the sample is random.

3. H_0: $\mu_A = \mu_B$
       H_1: $\mu_A \neq \mu_B$
       $\alpha = 0.01$
       Test statistic: V, the total number of runs.
       Computations: From Exercise 3 of the previous section we can write the sequence

       B B B B B A B B A A B A A A A A A

       for which $n_1 = 9$, $n_2 = 9$, and $v = 6$. Therefore, the P value is

       $P = P(V \leq 6$ when H_0 is true$) = 0.044 > 0.01$.
       Decision: Do not reject H_0.

5. H_0: Sample is random
       H_1: Sample is not random
       $\alpha = 0.05$
       Critical region: $z < -1.96$ and $z > 1.96$.
       Computations: We find $\bar{x} = 2.15$. Assigning plus and minus signs for observations above
       and below the median, respectively, we obtain $n_1 = 15$, $n_2 = 15$, and $v = 19$. Now,

$$\mu_V = \frac{(2)(15)(15)}{30} + 1 = 16,$$
$$\sigma_V^2 = \frac{(2)(15)(15)[(2)(15)(15) - 30]}{(30^2)(29)} = 7.241,$$

       and hence, $\sigma_V = 2.691$. Therefore,

       $z = (19 - 16)/2.691 = 1.11$.
       Decision: Do not reject H_0.

7. $n = 24$, $1 - \alpha = 0.90$. From Table A.19, $\gamma = 0.70$.

9. $n = 135$, $1 - \alpha = 0.95$. From Table A.20, $\gamma = 0.995$.

11. (a)

Ranks		
x	y	d
1	6	–5
2	1	1
3	16	–13
4	9.5	–5.5
5	18.5	–13.5
6	23	–17
7	8	–1
8	3	5
9	9.5	–0.5
10	16	–6
11	4	7
12	20	–8
13	11	2

Ranks		
x	y	d
14	12	2
15	2	13
16	6	10
17	13.5	3.5
18	13.5	4.5
19	16	3
20	23	–3
21	23	–2
22	23	–1
23	18.5	4.5
24	23	1
25	6	19

$$r_S = 1 - \frac{(6)(1586.5)}{(25)(625 - 1)} = 0.39.$$

(b) H_0: $\rho = 0$
H_1: $\rho \neq 0$
$\alpha = 0.05$
Critical region: $r_S < -0.400$ and $r_S > 0.400$.
Computations: $r_S = 0.39$.
Decisions: Do not reject H_0.

13. (a)

Weight	Chest size	d_i
3	6	–3
1	1	0
8	8	0
9	9	0
4	2	2
7	3	4
2	4	–2
6	7	–1
5	5	0

$$r_S = 1 - \frac{(6)(34)}{(9)(80)} = 0.72$$

(b) H_0: $\rho = 0$
H_1: $\rho > 0$
$\alpha = 0.025$
Critical region: $r_S > 0.683$.
Computations: $r_S = 0.72$.
Decision: Reject H_0, $\rho > 0$.

15. (a) $\sum d^2 = 24$, $r_s = 1 - \dfrac{(6)(24)}{(8)(63)} = 0.71$.

(b) H_0: $\rho = 0$
H_1 $\rho > 0$
$\alpha = 0.05$.
Critical region: $r_s > 0.643$.
Computations: $r_s = 0.71$.
Decision: Reject H_0, $\rho > 0$.